TWISTED
SUDOKU

This edition first published in 2018 by Ginger Fox®
an imprint of Hacche Retail Ltd
Unit 1-3, Dovecote Barn, Elkstone Studios, Elkstone
Cheltenham, GL53 9PQ, United Kingdom

www.gingerfox.co.uk

Follow us!
@GingerFoxUK
@GingerFoxUSA
Tweet us @GingerFox_UK

Puzzles created by Dr Gareth Moore at Any Puzzle Media

ISBN: 978-1-911006-40-4

10 9 8 7

Printed and bound in China

EU Authorised Representative:
CERTLabel U.G.
(haftungsbeschränkt)
Wichertstraße 16/17
10439
Berlin
Germany

What's the TWIST?

Take a standard sudoku...

	2		9				4	
4		9		1		8		6
	8				3		5	
		3	4	6	9			8
	1		7		5		9	
9			1	3	8	4		
	9		3				6	
1		6		7		5		9
	7				4		8	

Place a single digit into each empty square
so that every row, column and three-by-three box
contains each digit from the range 1 to 9.

Done this before?

Hundreds or thousands of times?

Are you ready to try something
a little bit DIFFERENT?

...then give it a TWIST!

Place a single digit into each empty square
so that every row, column and three-by-three box
contains each digit from the range 1 to 9...

...and now comes the INTERESTING bit!

This is a **Thermometer** sudoku. Some squares contain
part of a thermometer shape, and digits in these squares
must increase in value from the rounded bulb end
to the top. For example, 1 3 4 5 would be valid,
but 1 3 3 5 or 1 3 2 5 would not.

	2		9					
		9						6
						5		
				6				8
			7		5			
9				3				
	9							
1						5		
					4		8	

So, are you ready to brave the **Blackout**, kill the **Kropki** and trounce the **Trio**?

Turn the page to enter the warped world of **TWISTED** sudoku,
featuring a terrifying total of 110 puzzles that bend the rules in 18 deliriously different ways.

Instructions for the puzzles are at the top of each page.
If you need more help, **TWIST** the book to read the tips, but only read 'em if you need 'em!

Good luck from the **TWISTED** team... we think you might need it!

Solutions start on page 114!

What's the TWIST?

Place a single digit into each empty square so that every row, column and three-by-three box contains each digit from the range 1 to 9.

A set of four digits (quad marks) is shown on the intersection between some sets of four squares. These four digits must be placed into the four adjoining squares in an undisclosed order.

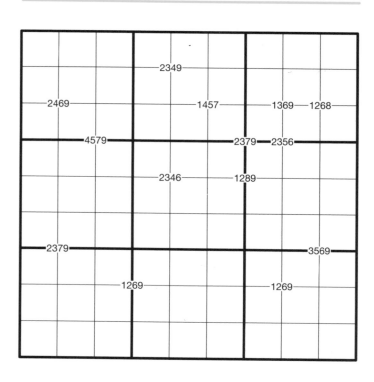

2. ODD-EVEN

What's the TWIST?

Place a single digit into each empty square so that every row, column and three-by-three box contains each digit from the range 1 to 9.

All squares that are shaded grey must contain even digits.

9	4	5	1	8	2	3	7	6
1	2	7	5	3	6	8	4	9
6	3	8	9	7	4	1	5	2
8	2	6	4	9	3	7	1	5
3	7	9	2	5	1	4	6	8
4	5	1	7	6	8	9	2	3
5	9	2	8	1	7	6	3	4
8	1	3	6	4	5	2	9	7
7	6	4	3	2	9	5	8	1

TWISTED tip: All even squares are marked so you can solve this as two separate puzzles, one even and one odd.

3. WRAPAROUND

What's the TWIST?

Place a single digit into each empty square so that every row, column and bold-lined jigsaw shape contains each digit from the range 1 to 9.

Some jigsaw shapes wrap around from one edge of the grid to the other (see breaks in bold lines). Jigsaw shapes continue at the start or end of the same row or column.

8						9
	8				4	
		6	3	1		
		1				
	1	6	4	8		
		7				
	9	8		3		
	5				3	
4						5

4. BLACKOUT

What's the TWIST?

Place a single digit into each empty white square so that every row, column and three-by-three box contains eight different digits from the range 1 to 9.

Do not place digits in the blacked-out squares. Each blacked-out square may represent a different digit in its row, column and three-by-three box.

7	2		9	8	3	1	4	6
6	8	3			5	9	7	2
9	4	5		2		3	8	
2	6	8	3	1	9			8
		1	4	7		2	3	9
		7	8	6	2		1	5
8	7	4		5			2	3
3	5	2		9				1
	1	9	2	3		5	6	4

TWISTED tip: In the top-right box, the two empty white squares must contain 7 and 8, meaning there is no 5 in this box.

What's the TWIST?

Place a single digit into each empty square so that every row, column and three-by-three box contains each digit from the range 1 to 9.

No touching pair of squares, including diagonal neighbours, may contain the same digit.

7	2	8	3	9	1	46	456	456
456	45	9	46	7	8	2	13	13
46	3	1	2	46	5	7	8	9
8	7	45	9		3	146		2
3	45	2			7	16	9	
1	9	26	5	22	4	3	7	8
45	8	7		35	6	9	2	
9	16	3			2	5		7
2	16	45	7	35	9	8		

6. JIGSAW

What's the TWIST?

Place a single digit into each empty square so that every row, column and bold-lined jigsaw shape contains each digit from the range 1 to 9.

		2	7			5	8	
	7			5		9		6
					5	7		
7		4		6		2		5
	5	3		7		4		
9		5		3		8		
		6	5			3		
5		9		4		6	7	
	9	7				1	5	

TWISTED tip: Shade each jigsaw shape in a different colour to help you to visualise the regions.

7. OUTSIDER

What's the TWIST?

Place a single digit into each empty square so that every row, column and three-by-three box contains each digit from the range 1 to 9.

The digits shown outside the grid must be placed in the nearest three squares in their row or column, but not necessarily in the order shown.

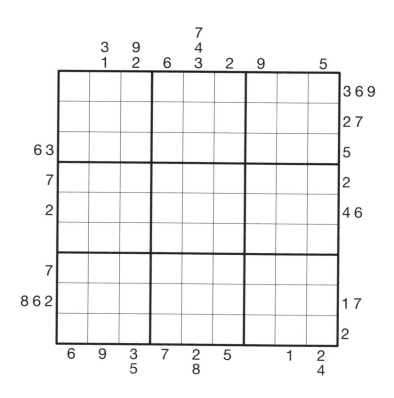

8. CONSECUTIVE

What's the TWIST?

Place a single digit into each empty square so that every row, column and three-by-three box contains each digit from the range 1 to 9.

The bars between pairs of squares show all pairs of adjacent squares with consecutive digits, meaning that they have a difference of 1, such as 4 and 5 or 8 and 9.

If there is no bar between a pair of squares, they are not consecutive.

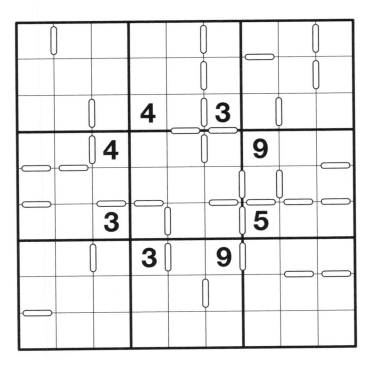

TWISTED tip: Start by looking for chains of consecutive squares, all linked with bars

9. KROPKI

What's the TWIST?

Place a single digit into each empty square so that every row, column and three-by-three box contains each digit from the range 1 to 9.

The white dots between pairs of squares show adjacent squares with consecutive digits, meaning that they have a difference of 1, such as 4 and 5 or 8 and 9.

The black dots between pairs of squares show adjacent squares in which the digit in one is exactly twice the value of the digit in the other.

If there is no dot between a pair of squares, they are not consecutive and one is not twice the value of the other.

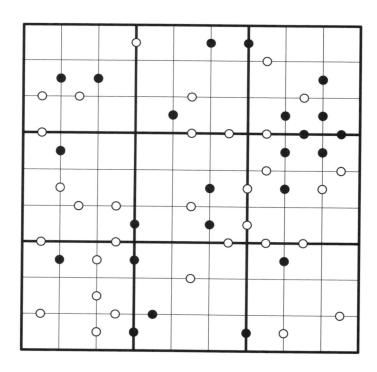

10. INEQUALITY

What's the TWIST?

Place a single digit into each empty square so that every row, column and three-by-three box contains each digit from the range 1 to 9.

The > symbol between pairs of squares indicates that the digit in one square is greater in value than the other. The arrow of the > always points towards the smaller digit.

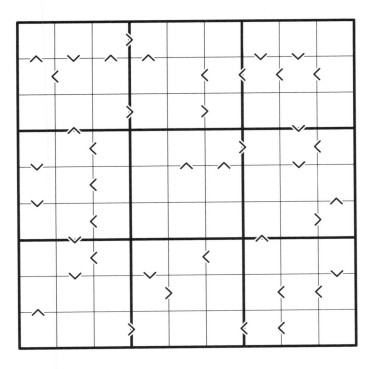

11. SLASHED

What's the TWIST?

Place a single digit into each empty square so that every row, column and three-by-three box contains each digit from the range 1 to 9.

No digit can repeat along the length of any of the diagonal lines slashed through the grid.

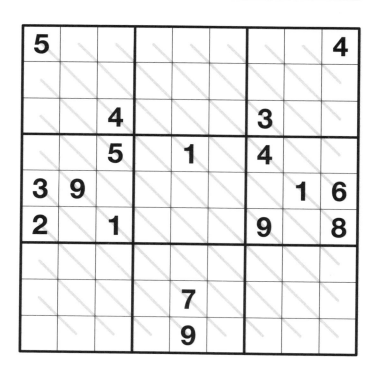

12. JIGSAW

What's the TWIST?

Place a single digit into each empty square so that every row, column and bold-lined jigsaw shape contains each digit from the range 1 to 9.

5

13. BLACKOUT

What's the TWIST?

Place a single digit into each empty white square so that every row, column and three-by-three box contains eight different digits from the range 1 to 9.

Do not place digits in the blacked-out squares. Each blacked-out square may represent a different digit in its row, column and three-by-three box.

2			3	6		7	4	1	5
7	9					5		6	2
6	1		3		2			9	
		1					5		
	5				4		6	8	
		2		5					
3	4		8		1				6
	2		5		4			3	1
1	6	9	7				2	5	4

14. TRIO

What's the TWIST?

Place a single digit into each empty square so that every row, column and three-by-three box contains each digit from the range 1 to 9.

Squares with a square inside always contain digits from 4 to 6.

Squares with a circle inside always contain digits from 7 to 9.

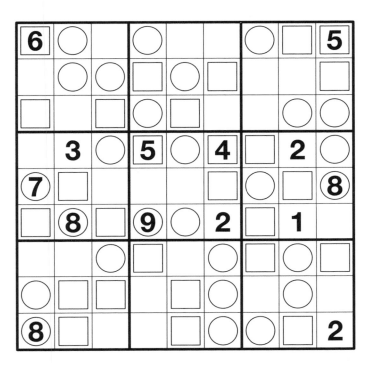

TWISTED tip: Look for the pre-placed digit that appears the most and start there, chasing it around the grid until you can make no further deductions.

15. XV

What's the TWIST?

Place a single digit into each empty square so that every row, column and three-by-three box contains each digit from the range 1 to 9.

The X and V symbols placed between some squares are Roman numerals representing the numbers 10 and 5 respectively. The X and V show all pairs of touching squares with digits that sum to either 10 or 5.

If there is no X or V between a pair of squares, they do not sum to 10 or 5.

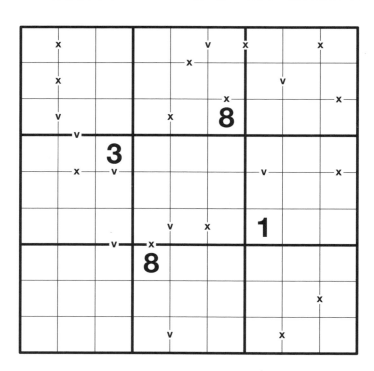

16. WRAPAROUND

What's the TWIST?

Place a single digit into each empty square so that every row, column and bold-lined jigsaw shape contains each digit from the range 1 to 9.

Some jigsaw shapes wrap around from one edge of the grid to the other (see breaks in bold lines). Jigsaw shapes continue at the start or end of the same row or column.

	9		7					6
2							9	
				6				
		5			2	8		
	6						5	
		9	5			4		
				3				
	3							7
9					4		8	

17. ARROWS

What's the TWIST?

Place a single digit into each empty square so that every row, column and three-by-three box contains each digit from the range 1 to 9.

Any digit in a square containing a circle must be equal to the sum of all of the digits along the path of the attached arrow.

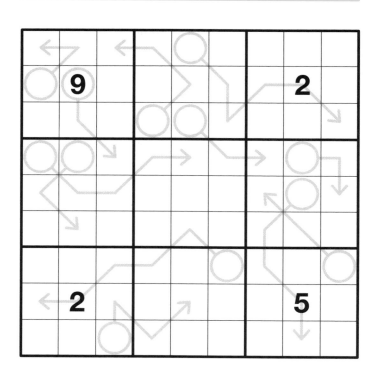

18. THERMOMETER

What's the TWIST?

Place a single digit into each empty square so that every row, column and three-by-three box contains each digit from the range 1 to 9.

Some squares contain part of a thermometer shape. Digits in these squares must increase in value from the rounded bulb end to the top. For example, 1 3 4 5 would be valid but 1 3 3 5 and 1 3 2 5 would not.

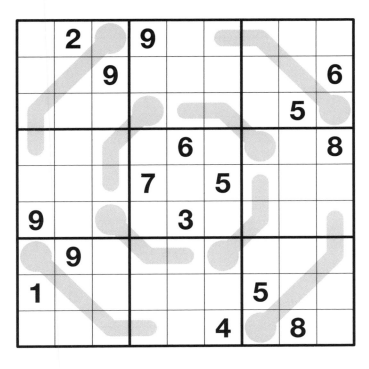

19. FRAME

What's the TWIST?

Place a single digit into each empty square so that every row, column and three-by-three box contains each digit from the range 1 to 9.

The numbers placed around the outside of the grid give the total of the digits in the three closest squares in their row or column.

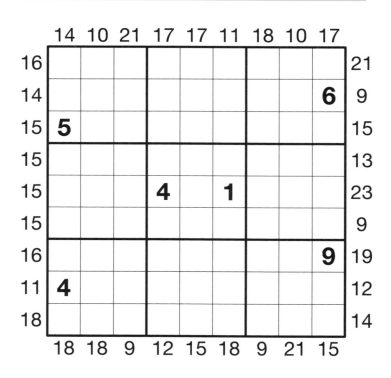

TWISTED tip: A 23 in the frame outside the grid means that the digits 9, 8 and 6 must be placed in the nearest three squares of that row or column.

22

20. CORNERED

What's the TWIST?

Place a single digit into each empty square so that every row, column and three-by-three box contains each digit from the range 1 to 9.

The greater-than symbol (>) placed in the corner of some squares shows that the digit in that square is higher than the digit in all three neighbouring squares.

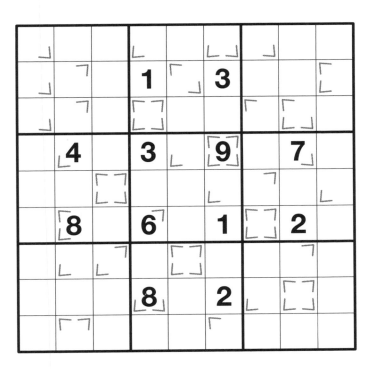

21. LITTLE KILLER

What's the TWIST?

Place a single digit into each empty square so that every row, column and three-by-three box contains each digit from the range 1 to 9.

Each of the numbers placed around the outside of the grid has a corresponding arrow that points along a diagonal line through the grid. The number outside the grid gives the total of the digits in the squares along that diagonal line.

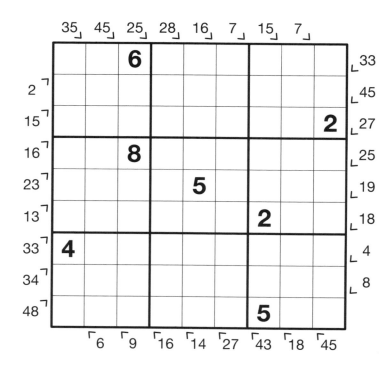

22. TOUCHY

What's the TWIST?

Place a single digit into each empty square so that every row, column and three-by-three box contains each digit from the range 1 to 9.

No touching pair of squares, including diagonal neighbours, may contain the same digit.

	1				5			8
2								
					8	7		
			9	4		1		
	4						3	
		3		1	2			
		6	7					
								4
8			6				1	

TWISTED tip: Even though this looks like a regular sudoku, don't forget the no-touching rule.

23. ODD-EVEN

What's the TWIST?

Place a single digit into each empty square so that every row, column and three-by-three box contains each digit from the range 1 to 9.

All squares that are shaded grey must contain even digits.

		4				5		
			3		7			
9								7
	3			7			6	
			8		3			
	4			6			5	
2								4
			9		1			
		1				9		

24. KROPKI

What's the TWIST?

Place a single digit into each empty square so that every row, column and three-by-three box contains each digit from the range 1 to 9.

The white dots between pairs of squares show adjacent squares with consecutive digits, meaning that they have a difference of 1, such as 4 and 5 or 8 and 9.

The black dots between pairs of squares show adjacent squares in which the digit in one is exactly twice the value of the digit in the other.

If there is no dot between a pair of squares, they are not consecutive and one is not twice the value of the other.

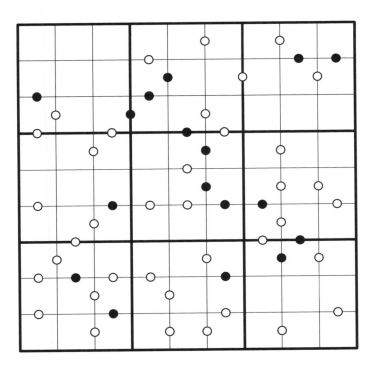

25. TRIO

What's the TWIST?

Place a single digit into each empty square so that every row, column and three-by-three box contains each digit from the range 1 to 9.

Squares with a square inside always contain digits from 4 to 6.

Squares with a circle inside always contain digits from 7 to 9.

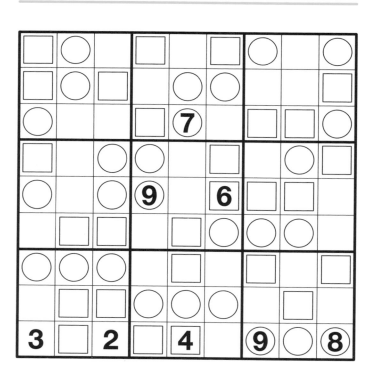

26. QUAD MARKS

What's the TWIST?

Place a single digit into each empty square so that every row, column and three-by-three box contains each digit from the range 1 to 9.

A set of four digits (quad marks) is shown on the intersection between some sets of four squares. These four digits must be placed into the four adjoining squares in an undisclosed order.

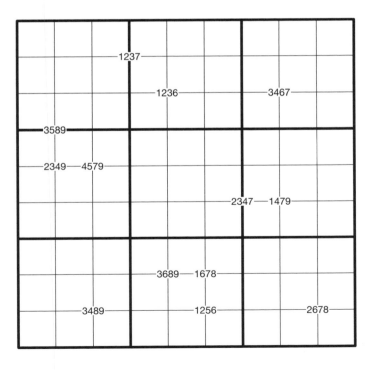

27. LITTLE KILLER

What's the TWIST?

Place a single digit into each empty square so that every row, column and three-by-three box contains each digit from the range 1 to 9.

Each of the numbers placed around the outside of the grid has a corresponding arrow that points along a diagonal line through the grid. The number outside the grid gives the total of the digits in the squares along that diagonal line.

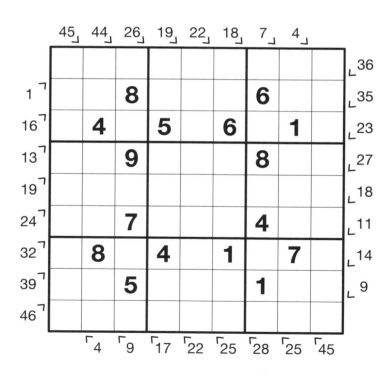

28. CONSECUTIVE

What's the TWIST?

Place a single digit into each empty square so that every row, column and three-by-three box contains each digit from the range 1 to 9.

The bars between pairs of squares show all pairs of adjacent squares with consecutive digits, meaning that they have a difference of 1, such as 4 and 5 or 8 and 9.

If there is no bar between a pair of squares, they are not consecutive.

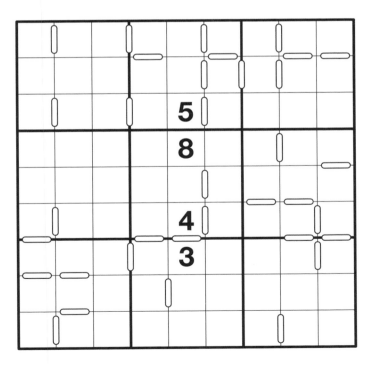

TWISTED tip: Two-by-two arrangements of squares that are all connected by bars must contain the same digit in at least one of the diagonal pairs.

29. INEQUALITY

What's the TWIST?

Place a single digit into each empty square so that every row, column and three-by-three box contains each digit from the range 1 to 9.

The > symbol between pairs of squares indicates that the digit in one square is greater in value than the other. The arrow of the > always points towards the smaller digit.

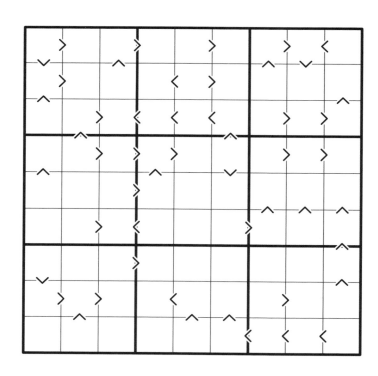

30. SLASHED

What's the TWIST?

Place a single digit into each empty square so that every row, column and three-by-three box contains each digit from the range 1 to 9.

No digit can repeat along the length of any of the diagonal lines slashed through the grid.

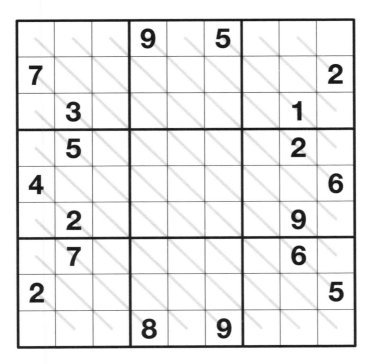

TWISTED tip: Only the central diagonal slash will contain every digit from the range 1 to 9. Use elimination-based logic for the shorter slashes.

31. TOUCHY

What's the TWIST?

Place a single digit into each empty square so that every row, column and three-by-three box contains each digit from the range 1 to 9.

No touching pair of squares, including diagonal neighbours, may contain the same digit.

3		9	8		5	6		1
	7						5	
5								4
9			5		1			7
4			6		8			2
6								8
	5						1	
8		4	7		3	2		5

TWISTED tip: Digits around the edges of the grid have fewer neighbours than central digits and provide less information. Focus on the inner squares first.

32. OUTSIDER

What's the TWIST?

Place a single digit into each empty square so that every row, column and three-by-three box contains each digit from the range 1 to 9.

The digits shown outside the grid must be placed in the nearest three squares in their row or column, but not necessarily in the order shown.

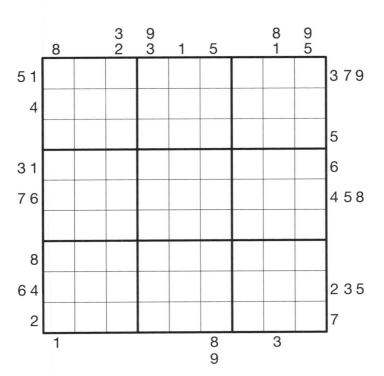

33. JIGSAW

What's the TWIST?

Place a single digit into each empty square so that every row, column and bold-lined jigsaw shape contains each digit from the range 1 to 9.

34. XV

What's the TWIST?

Place a single digit into each empty square so that every row, column and three-by-three box contains each digit from the range 1 to 9.

The X and V symbols placed between some squares are Roman numerals representing the numbers 10 and 5 respectively. The X and V show all pairs of touching squares with digits that sum to either 10 or 5.

If there is no X or V between a pair of squares, they do not sum to 10 or 5.

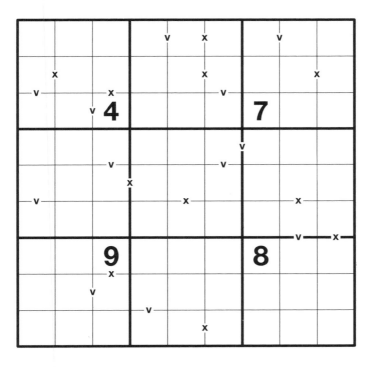

TWISTED tip: Squares linked with an X must contain 1 and 9, 2 and 8, 3 and 7 or 4 and 6.

35. ARROWS

What's the TWIST?

Place a single digit into each empty square so that every row, column and three-by-three box contains each digit from the range 1 to 9.

Any digit in a square containing a circle must be equal to the sum of all of the digits along the path of the attached arrow.

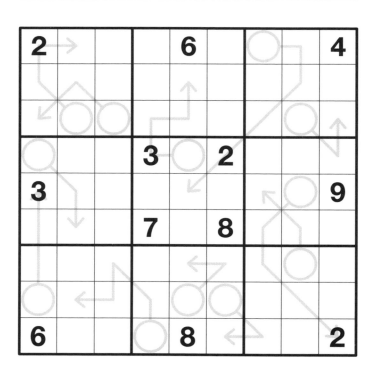

36. BLACKOUT

What's the TWIST?

Place a single digit into each empty white square so that every row, column and three-by-three box contains eight different digits from the range 1 to 9.

Do not place digits in the blacked-out squares. Each blacked-out square may represent a different digit in its row, column and three-by-three box.

	5		3	▓	6	2		
▓	1		5			9	6	3
7	3		9	1		▓		
5		▓		7		8	3	9
		6	4		5	7	▓	
3	9	1		6	▓			4
			8	2			9	▓
2	8	3	▓		7		4	
	▓	9	6		3		8	

TWISTED tip: A digit that couldn't be placed in a blacked-out square if it were white might still be the missing digit (remember; it can differ from row to column to box).

37. ODD-EVEN

What's the TWIST?

Place a single digit into each empty square so that every row, column and three-by-three box contains each digit from the range 1 to 9.

All squares that are shaded grey must contain even digits.

	4			3			1	
3					8			
				1				2
9		3					1	5
6				7				
			4					8
	5			9			4	

38. WRAPAROUND

What's the TWIST?

Place a single digit into each empty square so that every row, column and bold-lined jigsaw shape contains each digit from the range 1 to 9.

Some jigsaw shapes wrap around from one edge of the grid to the other (see breaks in bold lines). Jigsaw shapes continue at the start or end of the same row or column.

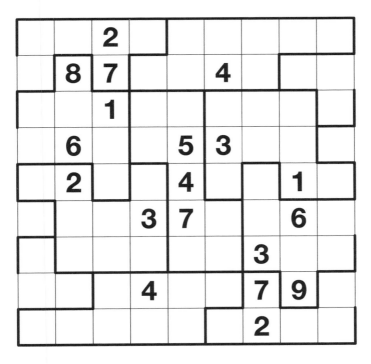

39. OUTSIDER

What's the TWIST?

Place a single digit into each empty square so that every row, column and three-by-three box contains each digit from the range 1 to 9.

The digits shown outside the grid must be placed in the nearest three squares in their row or column, but not necessarily in the order shown.

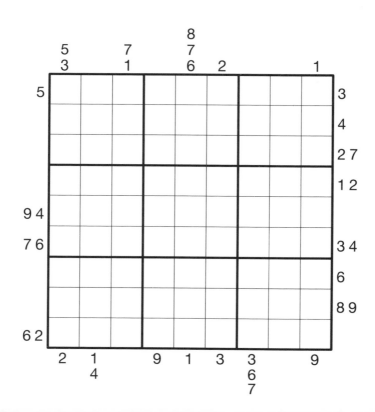

40. CORNERED

What's the TWIST?

Place a single digit into each empty square so that every row, column and three-by-three box contains each digit from the range 1 to 9.

The greater-than symbol (>) placed in the corner of some squares shows that the digit in that square is higher than the digit in all three neighbouring squares.

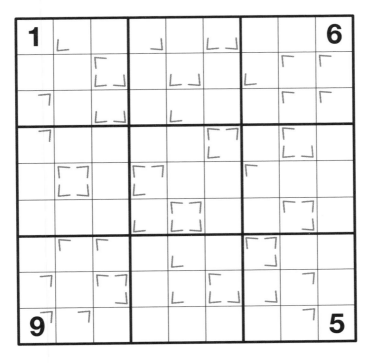

TWISTED tip: A low digit in a square with a greater-than symbol tells you a lot about the three neighbouring squares.

41. FRAME

What's the TWIST?

Place a single digit into each empty square so that every row, column and three-by-three box contains each digit from the range 1 to 9.

The numbers placed around the outside of the grid give the total of the digits in the three closest squares in their row or column.

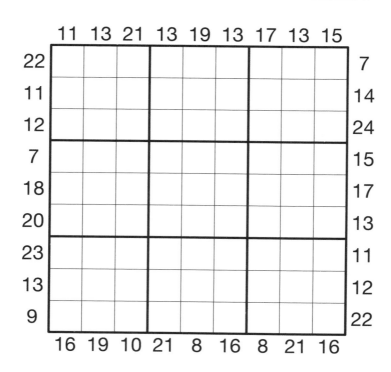

42. INEQUALITY

What's the TWIST?

Place a single digit into each empty square so that every row, column and three-by-three box contains each digit from the range 1 to 9.

The > symbol between pairs of squares indicates that the digit in one square is greater in value than the other. The arrow of the > always points towards the smaller digit.

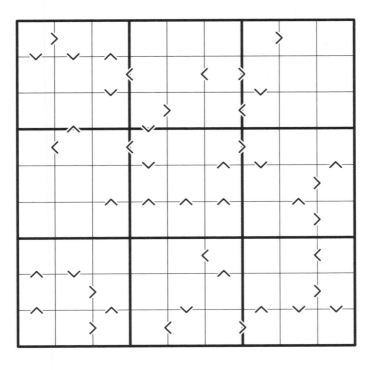

43. CONSECUTIVE

What's the TWIST?

Place a single digit into each empty square so that every row, column and three-by-three box contains each digit from the range 1 to 9.

The bars between pairs of squares show all pairs of adjacent squares with consecutive digits, meaning that they have a difference of 1, such as 4 and 5 or 8 and 9.

If there is no bar between a pair of squares, they are not consecutive.

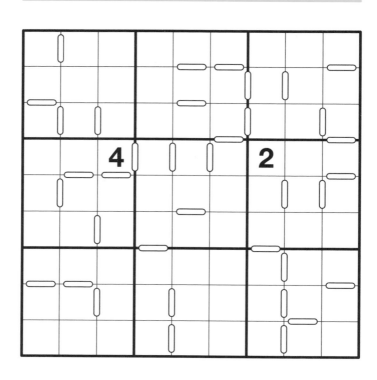

44. JIGSAW

What's the TWIST?

Place a single digit into each empty square so that every row, column and bold-lined jigsaw shape contains each digit from the range 1 to 9.

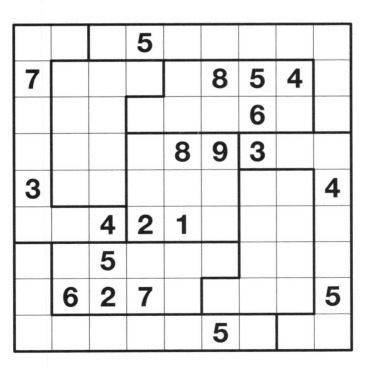

45. XV

What's the TWIST?

Place a single digit into each empty square so that every row, column and three-by-three box contains each digit from the range 1 to 9.

The X and V symbols placed between some squares are Roman numerals representing the numbers 10 and 5 respectively. The X and V show all pairs of touching squares with digits that sum to either 10 or 5.

If there is no X or V between a pair of squares, they do not sum to 10 or 5.

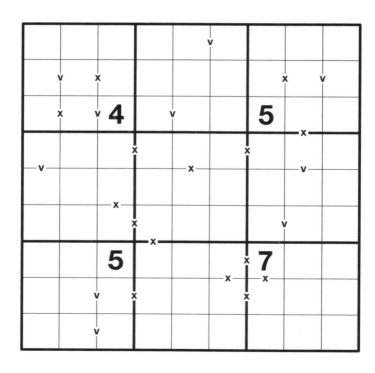

46. SLASHED

What's the TWIST?

Place a single digit into each empty square so that every row, column and three-by-three box contains each digit from the range 1 to 9.

No digit can repeat along the length of any of the diagonal lines slashed through the grid.

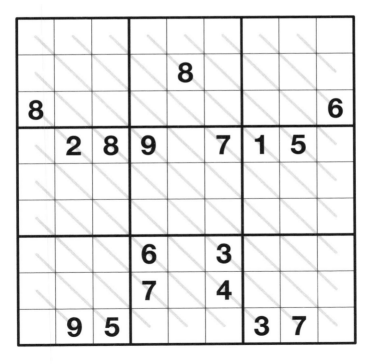

TWISTED tip: Make notes in pencil to keep track of which digits can fit in which squares. This will help you keep track of deductions that use the diagonal slashes.

47. THERMOMETER

What's the TWIST?

Place a single digit into each empty square so that every row, column and three-by-three box contains each digit from the range 1 to 9.

Some squares contain part of a thermometer shape. Digits in these squares must increase in value from the rounded bulb end to the top. For example, 1 3 4 5 would be valid but 1 3 3 5 and 1 3 2 5 would not.

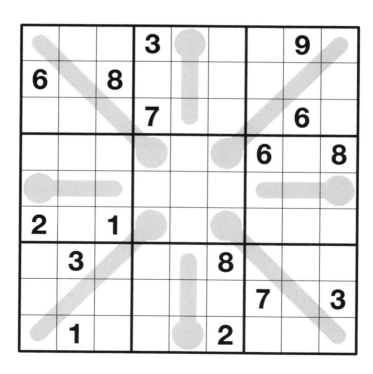

48. TRIO

What's the TWIST?

Place a single digit into each empty square so that every row, column and three-by-three box contains each digit from the range 1 to 9.

Squares with a square inside always contain digits from 4 to 6.

Squares with a circle inside always contain digits from 7 to 9.

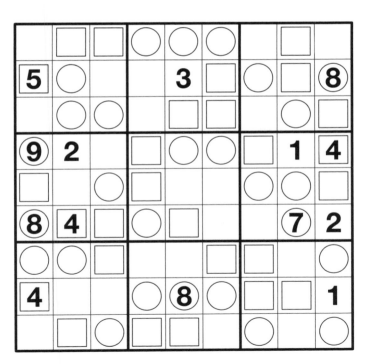

TWISTED tip: Try solving this grid as three separate puzzles: normal squares (digits 1 to 3), square squares (digits 4 to 6) and circle squares (digits 7 to 9).

49. TOUCHY

What's the TWIST?

Place a single digit into each empty square so that every row, column and three-by-three box contains each digit from the range 1 to 9.

No touching pair of squares, including diagonal neighbours, may contain the same digit.

			9		6			7
		4	2				1	3
							5	
	8	9					4	3
	7							
4	6				5	9		
9			4		7			

50. ARROWS

What's the TWIST?

Place a single digit into each empty square so that every row, column and three-by-three box contains each digit from the range 1 to 9.

Any digit in a square containing a circle must be equal to the sum of all of the digits along the path of the attached arrow.

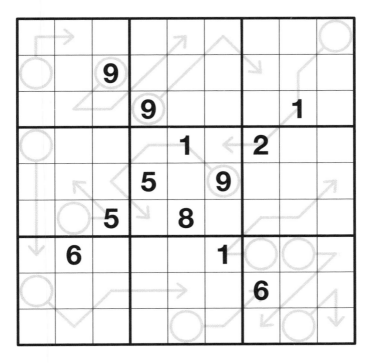

51. THERMOMETER

What's the TWIST?

Place a single digit into each empty square so that every row, column and three-by-three box contains each digit from the range 1 to 9.

Some squares contain part of a thermometer shape. Digits in these squares must increase in value from the rounded bulb end to the top. For example, 1 3 4 5 would be valid but 1 3 3 5 and 1 3 2 5 would not.

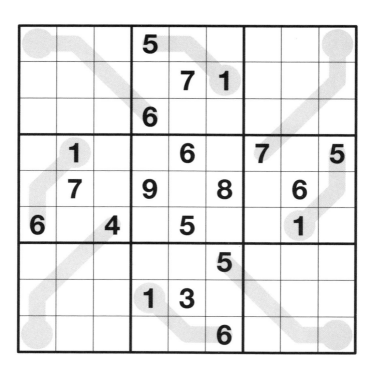

TWISTED tip: The longest thermometers provide the most information so focus on these first.

54

52. KROPKI

What's the TWIST?

Place a single digit into each empty square so that every row, column and three-by-three box contains each digit from the range 1 to 9.

The white dots between pairs of squares show adjacent squares with consecutive digits, meaning that they have a difference of 1, such as 4 and 5 or 8 and 9.

The black dots between pairs of squares show adjacent squares in which the digit in one is exactly twice the value of the digit in the other.

If there is no dot between a pair of squares, they are not consecutive and one is not twice the value of the other.

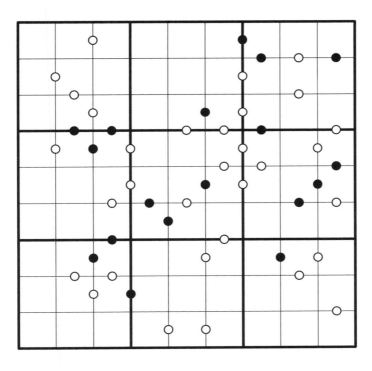

TWISTED tip: Even if you don't know exactly where a digit fits, if you can limit it to a few squares this may eliminate options from chains elsewhere in the grid.

53. QUAD MARKS

What's the TWIST?

Place a single digit into each empty square so that every row, column and three-by-three box contains each digit from the range 1 to 9.

A set of four digits (quad marks) is shown on the intersection between some sets of four squares. These four digits must be placed into the four adjoining squares in an undisclosed order.

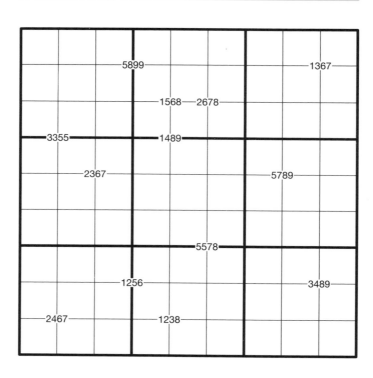

54. LITTLE KILLER

What's the TWIST?

Place a single digit into each empty square so that every row, column and three-by-three box contains each digit from the range 1 to 9.

Each of the numbers placed around the outside of the grid has a corresponding arrow that points along a diagonal line through the grid. The number outside the grid gives the total of the digits in the squares along that diagonal line.

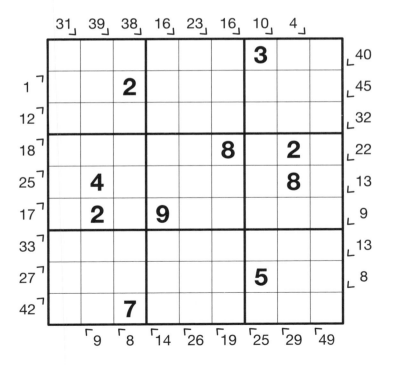

55. SLASHED

What's the TWIST?

Place a single digit into each empty square so that every row, column and three-by-three box contains each digit from the range 1 to 9.

No digit can repeat along the length of any of the diagonal lines slashed through the grid.

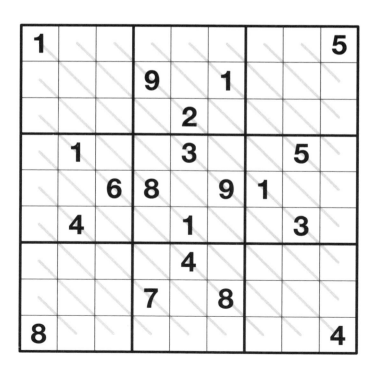

TWISTED tip: Focus on the squares along the longest diagonal slashes first.

What's the TWIST?

Place a single digit into each empty white square so that every row, column and three-by-three box contains eight different digits from the range 1 to 9.

Do not place digits in the blacked-out squares. Each blacked-out square may represent a different digit in its row, column and three-by-three box.

6			7			3	8	■
8	7		2		■		5	
9	■		5	6	3			
■		3		8		1	6	
1		5	6	■	2	8		9
	6	8		3		■		
			3	1	9		■	7
	3		■		5		2	8
5	8	■		2				4

TWISTED tip: If only one digit can be placed in a square, it must go there. In this situation you can forget about the blacked-out squares.

57. WRAPAROUND

What's the TWIST?

Place a single digit into each empty square so that every row, column and bold-lined jigsaw shape contains each digit from the range 1 to 9.

Some jigsaw shapes wrap around from one edge of the grid to the other (see breaks in bold lines). Jigsaw shapes continue at the start or end of the same row or column.

		9			6			
	1	7						5
							3	8
			2	3				
			6					
		4	1					
3	7							
6					2	1		
		2		5				

58. CONSECUTIVE

What's the TWIST?

Place a single digit into each empty square so that every row, column and three-by-three box contains each digit from the range 1 to 9.

The bars between pairs of squares show all pairs of adjacent squares with consecutive digits, meaning that they have a difference of 1, such as 4 and 5 or 8 and 9.

If there is no bar between a pair of squares, they are not consecutive.

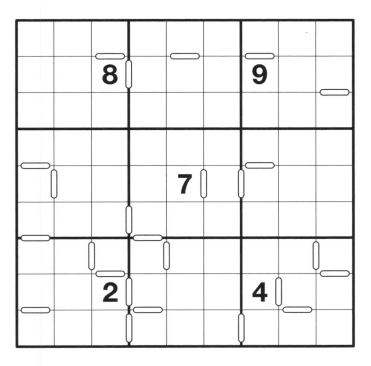

TWISTED tip: The absence of a bar between two squares is a critical tool in solving the puzzle.

59. CORNERED

What's the TWIST?

Place a single digit into each empty square so that every row, column and three-by-three box contains each digit from the range 1 to 9.

The greater-than symbol (>) placed in the corner of some squares shows that the digit in that square is higher than the digit in all three neighbouring squares.

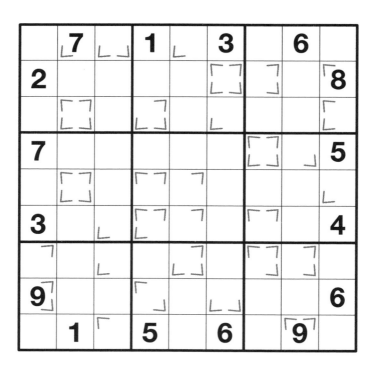

60. OUTSIDER

What's the TWIST?

Place a single digit into each empty square so that every row, column and three-by-three box contains each digit from the range 1 to 9.

The digits shown outside the grid must be placed in the nearest three squares in their row or column, but not necessarily in the order shown.

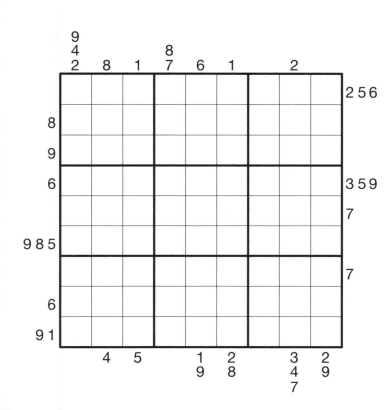

TWISTED tip: Cross-reference the outside clues. For example, a 7 at one end of a row means there can't be a 7 in that row in an intersecting column at the opposite end.

61. JIGSAW

What's the TWIST?

Place a single digit into each empty square so that every row, column and bold-lined jigsaw shape contains each digit from the range 1 to 9.

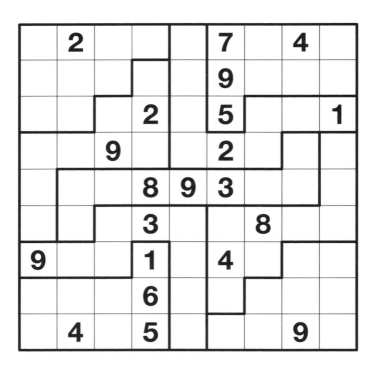

TWISTED tip: Make a note in pencil in each square of which digits can go there.

62. TOUCHY

What's the TWIST?

Place a single digit into each empty square so that every row, column and three-by-three box contains each digit from the range 1 to 9.

No touching pair of squares, including diagonal neighbours, may contain the same digit.

			8					
	6	3		2		8	4	
	9						6	
			7		8			
9	2						8	5
			2		4			
	5						2	
	8	1		3		5	9	
				1				

TWISTED tip: If you know a digit must go in one of two squares, you can exclude that digit from any square that touches both of those squares.

63. ARROWS

What's the TWIST?

Place a single digit into each empty square so that every row, column and three-by-three box contains each digit from the range 1 to 9.

Any digit in a square containing a circle must be equal to the sum of all of the digits along the path of the attached arrow.

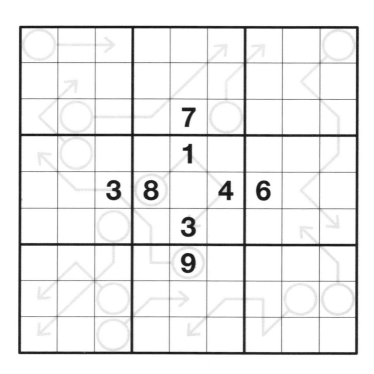

64. FRAME

What's the TWIST?

Place a single digit into each empty square so that every row, column and three-by-three box contains each digit from the range 1 to 9.

The numbers placed around the outside of the grid give the total of the digits in the three closest squares in their row or column.

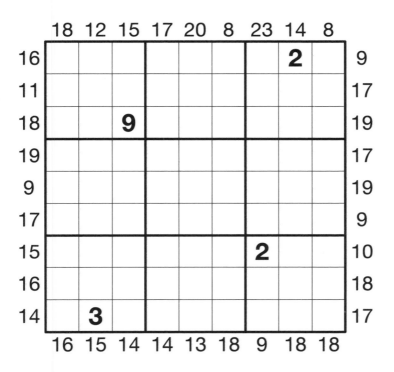

65. INEQUALITY

What's the TWIST?

Place a single digit into each empty square so that every row, column and three-by-three box contains each digit from the range 1 to 9.

The > symbol between pairs of squares indicates that the digit in one square is greater in value than the other. The arrow of the > always points towards the smaller digit.

TWISTED tip: Sequences of squares located within boxes that are connected by the greater-than symbol provide a lot of information, as you know that digits cannot repeat.

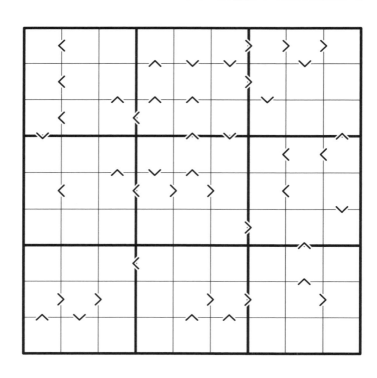

66. XV

What's the TWIST?

Place a single digit into each empty square so that every row, column and three-by-three box contains each digit from the range 1 to 9.

The X and V symbols placed between some squares are Roman numerals representing the numbers 10 and 5 respectively. The X and V show all pairs of touching squares with digits that sum to either 10 or 5.

If there is no X or V between a pair of squares, they do not sum to 10 or 5.

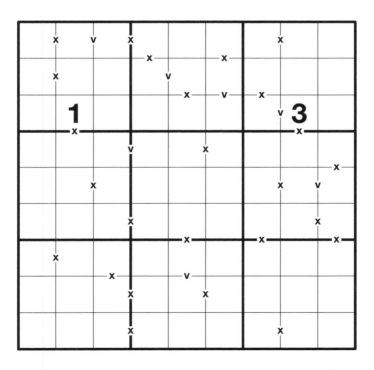

67. TRIO

What's the TWIST?

Place a single digit into each empty square so that every row, column and three-by-three box contains each digit from the range 1 to 9.

Squares with a square inside always contain digits from 4 to 6.

Squares with a circle inside always contain digits from 7 to 9.

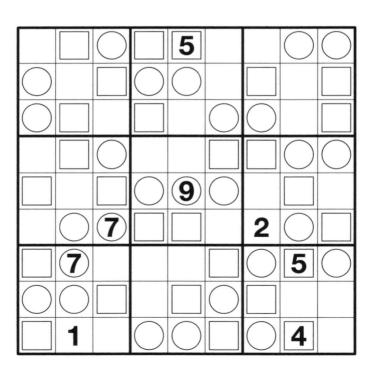

68. ODD-EVEN

What's the TWIST?

Place a single digit into each empty square so that every row, column and three-by-three box contains each digit from the range 1 to 9.

All squares that are shaded grey must contain even digits.

8			2	4				7
			8	7				
		7				9		
2	6						7	4
4	1						9	2
		4				7		
			1		9			
3			4		6			1

TWISTED tip: Start with rows, columns or boxes with a high proportion of either odd or even squares.

71

69. TOUCHY

What's the TWIST?

Place a single digit into each empty square so that every row, column and three-by-three box contains each digit from the range 1 to 9.

No touching pair of squares, including diagonal neighbours, may contain the same digit.

		9						
				7		1		
			6		8		2	3
	5					3		
		2				4		
		1					6	
5	8		4		9			
		3		1				
						9		

TWISTED tip: Look for digits that appear frequently in the grid. These will really restrict where else that digit can be placed.

72

70. XV

What's the TWIST?

Place a single digit into each empty square so that every row, column and three-by-three box contains each digit from the range 1 to 9.

The X and V symbols placed between some squares are Roman numerals representing the numbers 10 and 5 respectively. The X and V show all pairs of touching squares with digits that sum to either 10 or 5.

If there is no X or V between a pair of squares, they do not sum to 10 or 5.

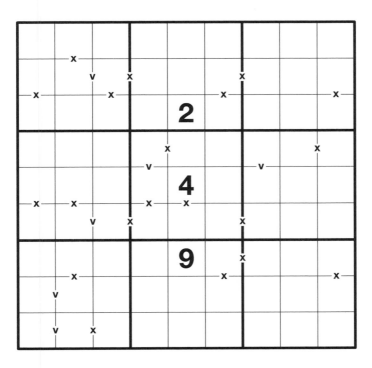

TWISTED tip: Remember to make deductions using the inverse rule – a lack of X or V means that two squares do not sum to either 10 or 5.

71. CONSECUTIVE

What's the TWIST?

Place a single digit into each empty square so that every row, column and three-by-three box contains each digit from the range 1 to 9.

The bars between pairs of squares show all pairs of adjacent squares with consecutive digits, meaning that they have a difference of 1, such as 4 and 5 or 8 and 9.

If there is no bar between a pair of squares, they are not consecutive.

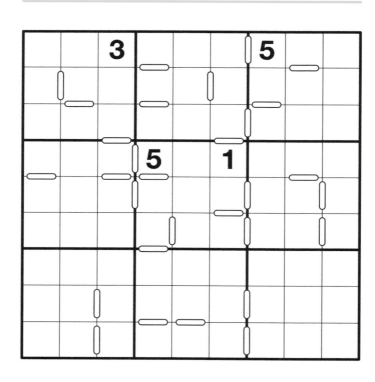

72. CORNERED

What's the TWIST?

Place a single digit into each empty square so that every row, column and three-by-three box contains each digit from the range 1 to 9.

The greater-than symbol (>) placed in the corner of some squares shows that the digit in that square is higher than the digit in all three neighbouring squares.

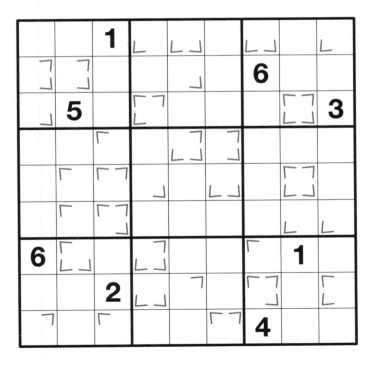

73. BLACKOUT

What's the TWIST?

Place a single digit into each empty white square so that every row, column and three-by-three box contains eight different digits from the range 1 to 9.

Do not place digits in the blacked-out squares. Each blacked-out square may represent a different digit in its row, column and three-by-three box.

6		9		▓		3		7
	1	4	7	9	6	2	8	▓
7	▓	8				5	9	4
	6		8		7		▓	
5	8			▓			4	2
▓	4		1		9		6	
9	5	▓				4	2	1
	7	2	9	1	8	▓	3	
1		6	▓	2		8		5

74. OUTSIDER

What's the TWIST?

Place a single digit into each empty square so that every row, column and three-by-three box contains each digit from the range 1 to 9.

The digits shown outside the grid must be placed in the nearest three squares in their row or column, but not necessarily in the order shown.

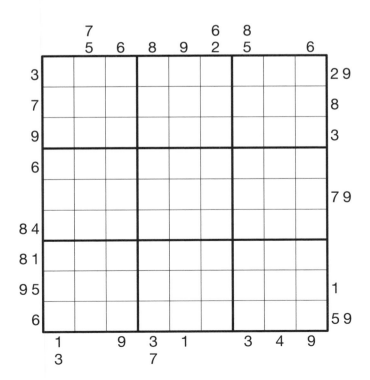

75. QUAD MARKS

What's the TWIST?

Place a single digit into each empty square so that every row, column and three-by-three box contains each digit from the range 1 to 9.

A set of four digits (quad marks) is shown on the intersection between some sets of four squares. These four digits must be placed into the four adjoining squares in an undisclosed order.

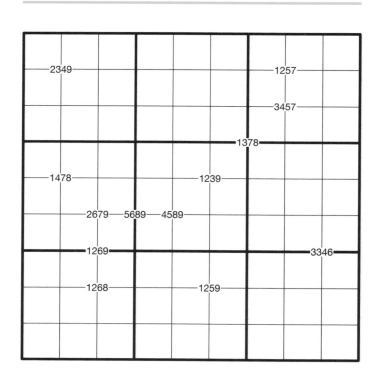

76. JIGSAW

What's the TWIST?

Place a single digit into each empty square so that every row, column and bold-lined jigsaw shape contains each digit from the range 1 to 9.

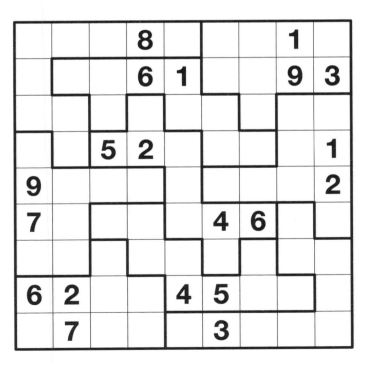

77. FRAME

What's the TWIST?

Place a single digit into each empty square so that every row, column and three-by-three box contains each digit from the range 1 to 9.

The numbers placed around the outside of the grid give the total of the digits in the three closest squares in their row or column.

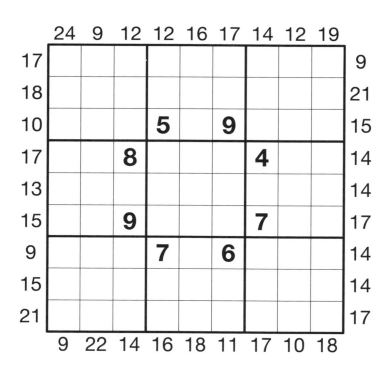

78. ARROWS

What's the TWIST?

Place a single digit into each empty square so that every row, column and three-by-three box contains each digit from the range 1 to 9.

Any digit in a square containing a circle must be equal to the sum of all of the digits along the path of the attached arrow.

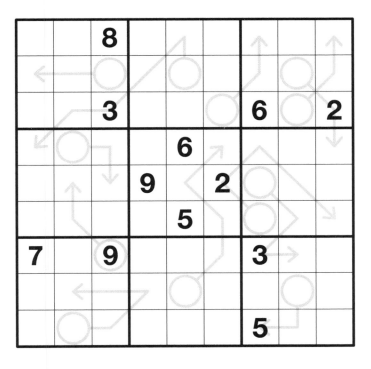

79. ODD-EVEN

What's the TWIST?

Place a single digit into each empty square so that every row, column and three-by-three box contains each digit from the range 1 to 9.

All squares that are shaded grey must contain even digits.

8				7				
				4	3			
9						8		
						5	2	
	9	2						
		1						5
			1	5				
				2				8

80. CONSECUTIVE

What's the TWIST?

Place a single digit into each empty square so that every row, column and three-by-three box contains each digit from the range 1 to 9.

The bars between pairs of squares show all pairs of adjacent squares with consecutive digits, meaning that they have a difference of 1, such as 4 and 5 or 8 and 9.

If there is no bar between a pair of squares, they are not consecutive.

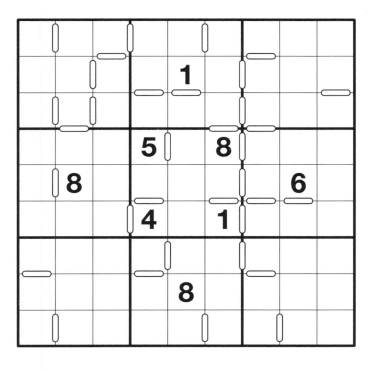

81. QUAD MARKS

What's the TWIST?

Place a single digit into each empty square so that every row, column and three-by-three box contains each digit from the range 1 to 9.

A set of four digits (quad marks) is shown on the intersection between some sets of four squares. These four digits must be placed into the four adjoining squares in an undisclosed order.

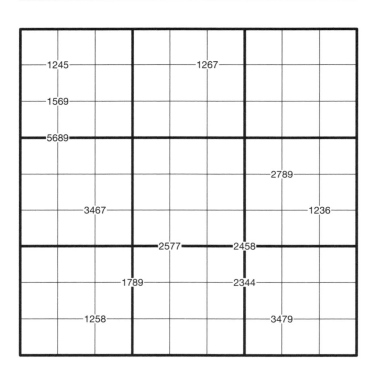

82. LITTLE KILLER

What's the TWIST?

Place a single digit into each empty square so that every row, column and three-by-three box contains each digit from the range 1 to 9.

Each of the numbers placed around the outside of the grid has a corresponding arrow that points along a diagonal line through the grid. The number outside the grid gives the total of the digits in the squares along that diagonal line.

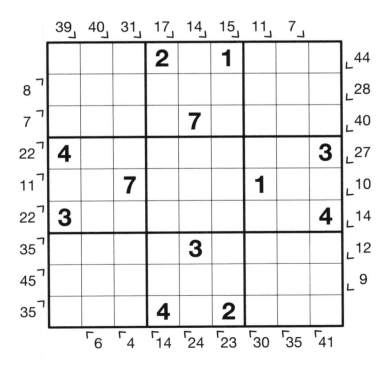

83. WRAPAROUND

What's the TWIST?

Place a single digit into each empty square so that every row, column and bold-lined jigsaw shape contains each digit from the range 1 to 9.

Some jigsaw shapes wrap around from one edge of the grid to the other (see breaks in bold lines). Jigsaw shapes continue at the start or end of the same row or column.

84. FRAME

What's the TWIST?

Place a single digit into each empty square so that every row, column and three-by-three box contains each digit from the range 1 to 9.

The numbers placed around the outside of the grid give the total of the digits in the three closest squares in their row or column.

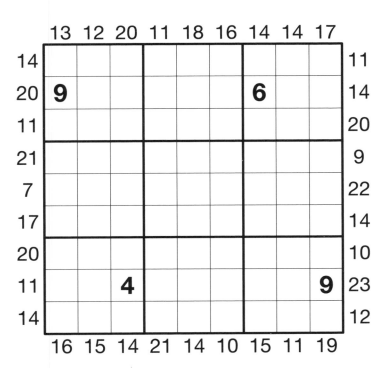

TWISTED tip: Start with one of the four corner three-by-three boxes, in which you can most easily cross-reference information from rows and columns with the framing digits.

85. ARROWS

What's the TWIST?

Place a single digit into each empty square so that every row, column and three-by-three box contains each digit from the range 1 to 9.

Any digit in a square containing a circle must be equal to the sum of all of the digits along the path of the attached arrow.

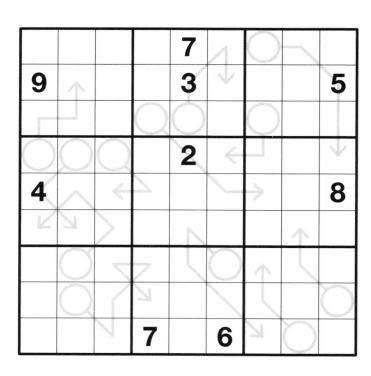

86. TOUCHY

What's the TWIST?

Place a single digit into each empty square so that every row, column and three-by-three box contains each digit from the range 1 to 9.

No touching pair of squares, including diagonal neighbours, may contain the same digit.

6			9		7			3
				2				
			5	4	3			
8		3				5		4
	1	5				3	8	
4		9				2		6
			4	6	1			
				3				
5			7		2			8

TWISTED tip: Look for chains of deductions with touching digits. You may be able to ripple observations across the puzzle.

87. JIGSAW

What's the TWIST?

Place a single digit into each empty square so that every row, column and bold-lined jigsaw shape contains each digit from the range 1 to 9.

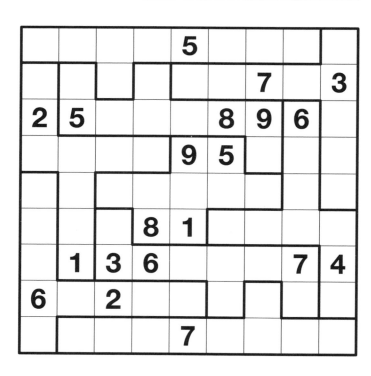

88. SLASHED

What's the TWIST?

Place a single digit into each empty square so that every row, column and three-by-three box contains each digit from the range 1 to 9.

No digit can repeat along the length of any of the diagonal lines slashed through the grid.

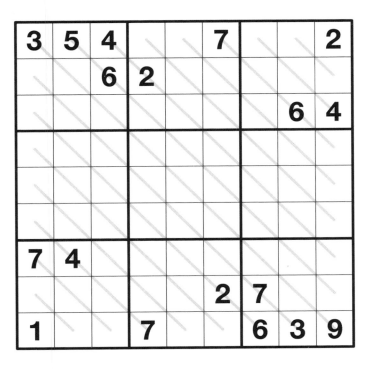

89. INEQUALITY

What's the TWIST?

Place a single digit into each empty square so that every row, column and three-by-three box contains each digit from the range 1 to 9.

The > symbol between pairs of squares indicates that the digit in one square is greater in value than the other. The arrow of the > always points towards the smaller digit.

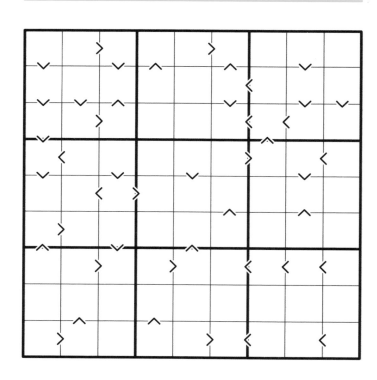

TWISTED tip: Look for squares with values lower than multiple other squares. These must contain low digits.

92

90. BLACKOUT

What's the TWIST?

Place a single digit into each empty white square so that every row, column and three-by-three box contains eight different digits from the range 1 to 9.

Do not place digits in the blacked-out squares. Each blacked-out square may represent a different digit in its row, column and three-by-three box.

		1	■	7	4	6		
	4	6		9	5	1	■	
9	■				1		2	4
3	5	9		8		■		7
6	1		4	■	9		8	2
8		■		1		5	4	9
1	7		9				3	■
■	8	2	7	6		4	5	
		3	1	5	■	9		

TWISTED tip: If you deduce which digit is missing from a particular row, column or box, you can then solve the rest of that region as normal.

91. XV

What's the TWIST?

Place a single digit into each empty square so that every row, column and three-by-three box contains each digit from the range 1 to 9.

The X and V symbols placed between some squares are Roman numerals representing the numbers 10 and 5 respectively. The X and V show all pairs of touching squares with digits that sum to either 10 or 5.

If there is no X or V between a pair of squares, they do not sum to 10 or 5.

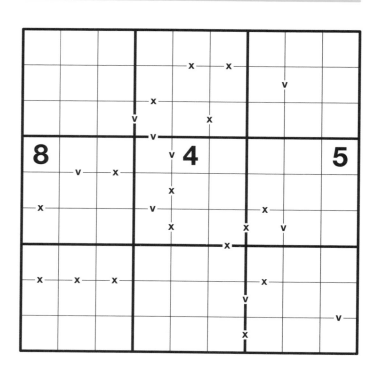

92. CORNERED

What's the TWIST?

Place a single digit into each empty square so that every row, column and three-by-three box contains each digit from the range 1 to 9.

The greater-than symbol (>) placed in the corner of some squares shows that the digit in that square is higher than the digit in all three neighbouring squares.

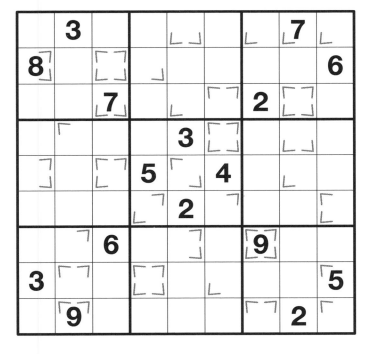

TWISTED tip: Where squares point to other squares that also contain arrows, you can build chains of possible values to further limit what digits can fit into those squares.

93. OUTSIDER

What's the TWIST?

Place a single digit into each empty square so that every row, column and three-by-three box contains each digit from the range 1 to 9.

The digits shown outside the grid must be placed in the nearest three squares in their row or column, but not necessarily in the order shown.

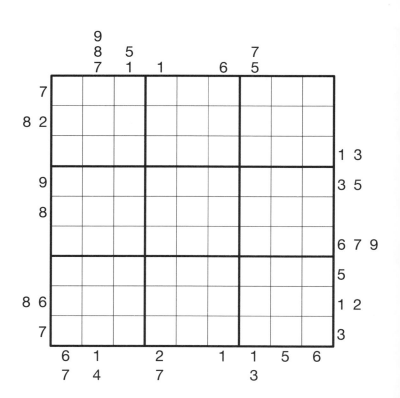

94. FRAME

What's the TWIST?

Place a single digit into each empty square so that every row, column and three-by-three box contains each digit from the range 1 to 9.

The numbers placed around the outside of the grid give the total of the digits in the three closest squares in their row or column.

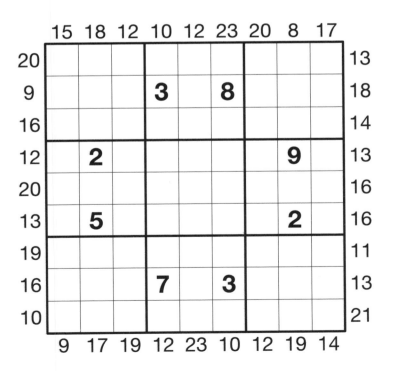

95. CONSECUTIVE

What's the TWIST?

Place a single digit into each empty square so that every row, column and three-by-three box contains each digit from the range 1 to 9.

The bars between pairs of squares show all pairs of adjacent squares with consecutive digits, meaning that they have a difference of 1, such as 4 and 5 or 8 and 9.

If there is no bar between a pair of squares, they are not consecutive.

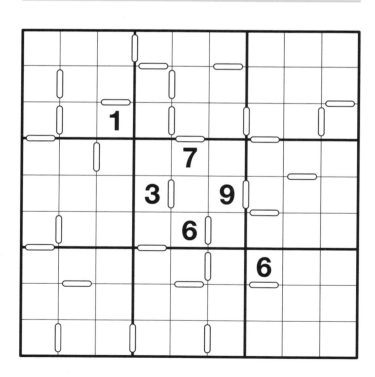

96. WRAPAROUND

What's the TWIST?

Place a single digit into each empty square so that every row, column and bold-lined jigsaw shape contains each digit from the range 1 to 9.

Some jigsaw shapes wrap around from one edge of the grid to the other (see breaks in bold lines). Jigsaw shapes continue at the start or end of the same row or column.

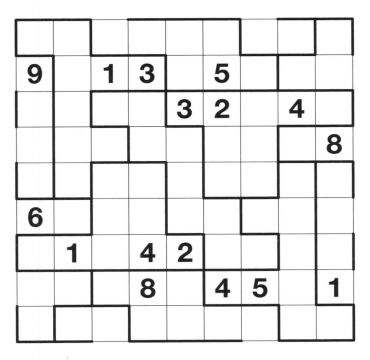

97. THERMOMETER

What's the TWIST?

Place a single digit into each empty square so that every row, column and three-by-three box contains each digit from the range 1 to 9.

Some squares contain part of a thermometer shape. Digits in these squares must increase in value from the rounded bulb end to the top. For example, 1 3 4 5 would be valid but 1 3 3 5 and 1 3 2 5 would not.

98. ARROWS

What's the TWIST?

Place a single digit into each empty square so that every row, column and three-by-three box contains each digit from the range 1 to 9.

Any digit in a square containing a circle must be equal to the sum of all of the digits along the path of the attached arrow.

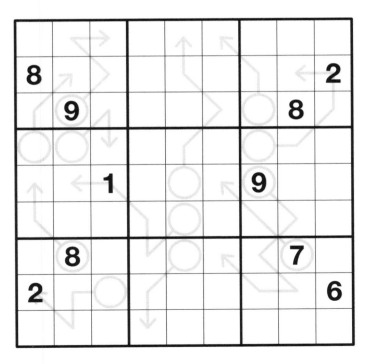

99. KROPKI

What's the TWIST?

Place a single digit into each empty square so that every row, column and three-by-three box contains each digit from the range 1 to 9.

The white dots between pairs of squares show adjacent squares with consecutive digits, meaning that they have a difference of 1, such as 4 and 5 or 8 and 9.

The black dots between pairs of squares show adjacent squares in which the digit in one is exactly twice the value of the digit in the other.

If there is no dot between a pair of squares, they are not consecutive and one is not twice the value of the other.

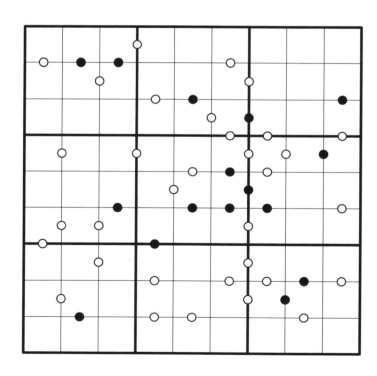

TWISTED tip: Chains of dots contained entirely within a row, column or box can be very useful as you know that digits cannot repeat within these regions.

102

100. XV

What's the TWIST?

Place a single digit into each empty square so that every row, column
and three-by-three box contains each digit from the range 1 to 9.

The X and V symbols placed between some squares are Roman
numerals representing the numbers 10 and 5 respectively.
The X and V show all pairs of touching squares with digits that
sum to either 10 or 5.

If there is no X or V between a pair of squares, they do not sum
to 10 or 5.

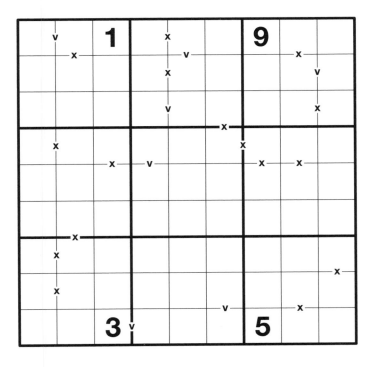

101. TOUCHY

What's the TWIST?

Place a single digit into each empty square so that every row, column and three-by-three box contains each digit from the range 1 to 9.

No touching pair of squares, including diagonal neighbours, may contain the same digit.

5						4	8	6
4			3					
1			4					
				2		7	1	
			5		9			
	6	4		7				
					5			1
					3			5
7	2	5						3

102. SLASHED

What's the TWIST?

Place a single digit into each empty square so that every row, column and three-by-three box contains each digit from the range 1 to 9.

No digit can repeat along the length of any of the diagonal lines slashed through the grid.

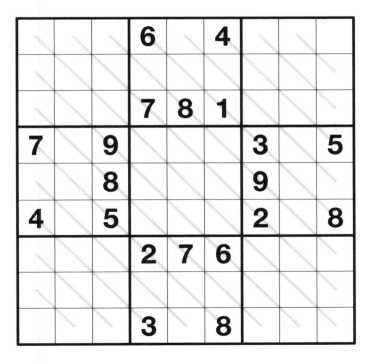

103. INEQUALITY

What's the TWIST?

Place a single digit into each empty square so that every row, column and three-by-three box contains each digit from the range 1 to 9.

The > symbol between pairs of squares indicates that the digit in one square is greater in value than the other. The arrow of the > always points towards the smaller digit.

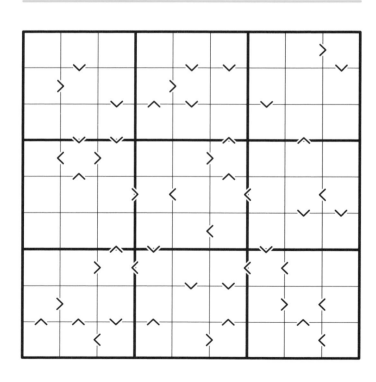

104. CONSECUTIVE

What's the TWIST?

Place a single digit into each empty square so that every row, column and three-by-three box contains each digit from the range 1 to 9.

The bars between pairs of squares show all pairs of adjacent squares with consecutive digits, meaning that they have a difference of 1, such as 4 and 5 or 8 and 9.

If there is no bar between a pair of squares, they are not consecutive.

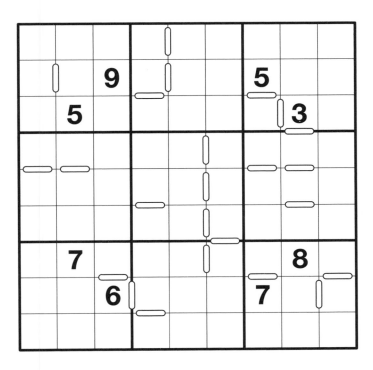

105. QUAD MARKS

What's the TWIST?

Place a single digit into each empty square so that every row, column and three-by-three box contains each digit from the range 1 to 9.

A set of four digits (quad marks) is shown on the intersection between some sets of four squares. These four digits must be placed into the four adjoining squares in an undisclosed order.

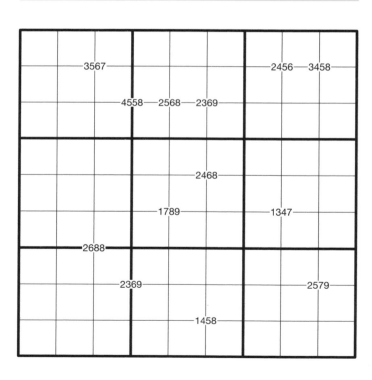

106. ODD-EVEN

What's the TWIST?

Place a single digit into each empty square so that every row, column and three-by-three box contains each digit from the range 1 to 9.

All squares that are shaded grey must contain even digits.

1				4				5
		2				1		
	9						2	
9				2				7
	4						7	
		7				6		
8				5				4

TWISTED tip: Focus on the digit that appears most frequently in the grid and attempt to place all the remaining instances of that digit.

107. JIGSAW

What's the TWIST?

Place a single digit into each empty square so that every row, column and bold-lined jigsaw shape contains each digit from the range 1 to 9.

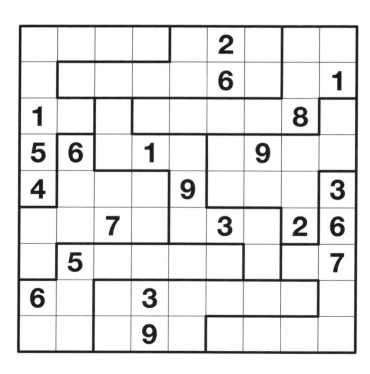

108. CORNERED

What's the TWIST?

Place a single digit into each empty square so that every row, column and three-by-three box contains each digit from the range 1 to 9.

The greater-than symbol (>) placed in the corner of some squares shows that the digit in that square is higher than the digit in all three neighbouring squares.

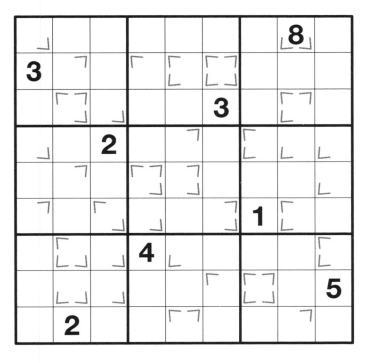

109. ARROWS

What's the TWIST?

Place a single digit into each empty square so that every row, column and three-by-three box contains each digit from the range 1 to 9.

Any digit in a square containing a circle must be equal to the sum of all of the digits along the path of the attached arrow.

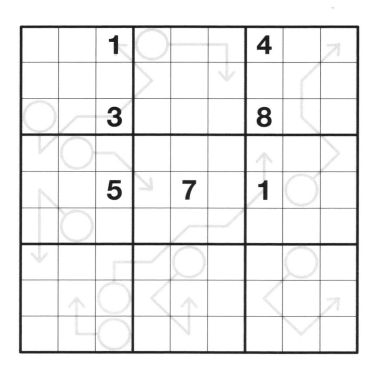

110. XV

What's the TWIST?

Place a single digit into each empty square so that every row, column and three-by-three box contains each digit from the range 1 to 9.

The X and V symbols placed between some squares are Roman numerals representing the numbers 10 and 5 respectively. The X and V show all pairs of touching squares with digits that sum to either 10 or 5.

If there is no X or V between a pair of squares, they do not sum to 10 or 5.

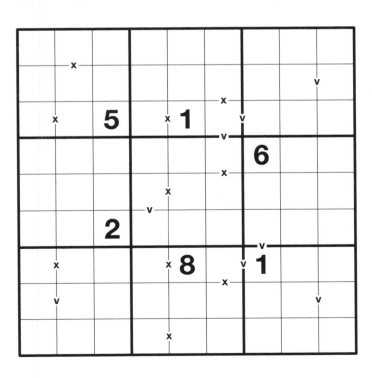

SOLUTIONS

Page 4 — 1. QUAD MARKS

3	1	8	2	9	6	5	4	7
2	6	7	3	4	5	9	1	8
4	9	5	8	1	7	3	6	2
8	7	4	6	3	9	2	5	1
6	5	3	4	2	1	8	7	9
9	2	1	7	5	8	4	3	6
7	3	2	1	8	4	6	9	5
5	8	6	9	7	3	1	2	4
1	4	9	5	6	2	7	8	3

Page 5 — 2. ODD-EVEN

9	4	5	1	8	2	3	7	6
1	2	7	5	3	6	8	4	9
6	3	8	9	7	4	1	5	2
2	8	6	4	9	3	7	1	5
3	7	9	2	5	1	4	6	8
4	5	1	7	6	8	9	2	3
5	9	2	8	1	7	6	3	4
8	1	3	6	4	5	2	9	7
7	6	4	3	2	9	5	8	1

Page 6 — 3. WRAPAROUND

8	3	5	1	4	7	6	2	9
1	8	2	7	6	9	5	4	3
2	4	6	5	3	8	1	9	7
5	7	8	9	1	3	2	6	4
3	9	1	6	5	4	8	7	2
9	1	3	2	7	6	4	5	8
7	2	9	4	8	5	3	1	6
6	5	4	8	9	2	7	3	1
4	6	7	3	2	1	9	8	5

Page 7 — 4. BLACKOUT

7	2		9	8	3	1	4	6
6	3	8	1		5	9	7	2
9	4	5	7	2	6	3	8	
2	6	7	3	1	9	4		8
5	8	1	4	7		2	3	9
4		3	8	6	2	7	1	5
8	7	4	6	5	1		2	3
3	5	2		4	7	8	9	1
	1	9	2	3	8	5	6	4

Page 8 — 5. TOUCHY

7	2	8	3	9	1	6	5	4
4	5	9	6	7	8	2	1	3
6	3	1	2	4	5	7	8	9
8	7	5	9	1	3	4	6	2
3	4	2	8	6	7	1	9	5
1	9	6	5	2	4	3	7	8
5	8	7	4	3	6	9	2	1
9	6	3	1	8	2	5	4	7
2	1	4	7	5	9	8	3	6

Page 9 — 6. JIGSAW

3	6	2	7	9	1	5	8	4
8	7	1	2	5	4	9	3	6
6	4	8	9	2	5	7	1	3
7	3	4	1	6	8	2	9	5
1	5	3	6	7	9	4	2	8
9	1	5	4	3	2	8	6	7
2	8	6	5	1	7	3	4	9
5	2	9	8	4	3	6	7	1
4	9	7	3	8	6	1	5	2

Page 10 — 7. OUTSIDER

8	7	2	5	4	1	9	3	6
5	1	9	6	3	8	2	4	7
4	3	6	9	7	2	1	8	5
9	5	7	8	6	4	3	2	1
2	8	1	3	5	7	4	6	9
3	6	4	2	1	9	5	7	8
7	9	3	1	2	6	8	5	4
6	2	8	4	9	5	7	1	3
1	4	5	7	8	3	6	9	2

Page 11 — 8. CONSECUTIVE

3	4	7	1	5	6	2	8	9
6	2	5	7	9	8	1	4	3
1	8	9	4	2	3	6	7	5
7	5	4	6	3	2	9	1	8
8	6	2	9	1	5	4	3	7
9	1	3	8	7	4	5	2	6
2	7	6	3	4	9	8	5	1
4	9	1	5	8	7	3	6	2
5	3	8	2	6	1	7	9	4

9. KROPKI

3	1	6	7	2	4	8	5	9
8	4	2	9	5	1	7	3	6
7	5	9	3	6	8	1	2	4
6	3	1	5	7	9	2	4	8
9	8	5	1	4	2	3	6	7
2	7	4	8	3	6	5	9	1
1	2	3	6	9	7	4	8	5
4	6	7	2	8	5	9	1	3
5	9	8	4	1	3	6	7	2

10. INEQUALITY

1	9	4	3	5	8	7	6	2
3	6	7	9	1	2	4	5	8
5	2	8	6	7	4	3	9	1
7	4	5	2	8	6	1	3	9
6	1	3	5	9	7	8	2	4
2	8	9	4	3	1	5	7	6
4	5	6	8	2	3	9	1	7
8	3	1	7	6	9	2	4	5
9	7	2	1	4	5	6	8	3

11. SLASHED

5	6	2	3	8	1	7	9	4
1	3	7	4	5	9	8	6	2
9	8	4	2	6	7	3	5	1
6	7	5	9	1	8	4	2	3
3	9	8	7	2	4	5	1	6
2	4	1	5	3	6	9	7	8
7	5	6	8	4	2	1	3	9
4	2	9	1	7	3	6	8	5
8	1	3	6	9	5	2	4	7

12. JIGSAW

2	3	1	5	7	9	8	4	6
6	5	4	1	8	3	9	7	2
8	9	7	4	6	2	5	1	3
4	7	8	6	2	1	3	9	5
5	1	3	8	9	6	4	2	7
9	2	6	7	3	4	1	5	8
7	6	5	9	1	8	2	3	4
1	8	2	3	4	5	7	6	9
3	4	9	2	5	7	6	8	1

13. BLACKOUT

2		3	6	9	7	4	1	5
7	9	8		1	5	3	6	2
6	1	4	3	8	2	7	9	
4	7	1	9		8	5	2	3
9	5		2	4	3	6	8	7
8	3	2	1	5	6		4	9
3	4	5	8	2	1	9		6
	2	7	5	6	4	8	3	1
1	6	9	7	3		2	5	4

14. TRIO

6	9	3	7	2	1	8	4	5
2	7	8	4	9	5	1	3	6
4	1	5	8	6	3	2	7	9
1	3	9	5	8	4	6	2	7
7	4	2	1	3	6	9	5	8
5	8	6	9	7	2	4	1	3
3	2	7	6	1	8	5	9	4
9	6	4	2	5	7	3	8	1
8	5	1	3	4	9	7	6	2

15. XV

8	2	6	5	4	1	9	3	7
3	7	5	9	6	2	4	1	8
1	4	9	3	7	8	5	6	2
5	1	3	6	8	9	2	7	4
7	9	2	1	5	4	3	8	6
6	8	4	2	3	7	1	5	9
2	5	1	8	9	6	7	4	3
4	3	8	7	2	5	6	9	1
9	6	7	4	1	3	8	2	5

16. WRAPAROUND

5	9	3	7	1	8	2	4	6
2	1	6	4	5	3	7	9	8
8	4	7	9	6	1	5	3	2
1	7	5	3	4	2	8	6	9
4	6	2	8	9	7	1	5	3
3	8	9	5	2	6	4	7	1
7	5	8	1	3	9	6	2	4
6	3	4	2	8	5	9	1	7
9	2	1	6	7	4	3	8	5

SOLUTIONS

Page 20 — 17. ARROWS

2	6	1	3	9	5	8	7	4
8	9	7	6	4	1	3	2	5
4	3	5	8	7	2	9	6	1
9	7	6	5	1	3	4	8	2
3	1	2	4	8	7	5	9	6
5	4	8	9	2	6	1	3	7
7	5	3	1	6	9	2	4	8
1	2	4	7	3	8	6	5	9
6	8	9	2	5	4	7	1	3

Page 21 — 18. THERMOMETER

5	2	1	9	8	6	3	4	7
4	3	9	5	1	7	8	2	6
6	8	7	2	4	3	9	5	1
7	5	3	4	6	9	2	1	8
8	1	4	7	2	5	6	9	3
9	6	2	1	3	8	4	7	5
2	9	8	3	5	1	7	6	4
1	4	6	8	7	2	5	3	9
3	7	5	6	9	4	1	8	2

Page 22 — 19. FRAME

2	6	8	3	1	4	9	5	7
7	3	4	8	9	5	1	2	6
5	1	9	6	7	2	8	3	4
1	8	6	5	3	9	7	4	2
3	5	7	4	2	1	6	9	8
9	4	2	7	8	6	5	1	3
8	7	1	2	5	3	4	6	9
4	2	5	9	6	7	3	8	1
6	9	3	1	4	8	2	7	5

Page 23 — 20. CORNERED

9	2	1	5	6	8	7	3	4
8	5	4	1	7	3	2	6	9
7	6	3	9	2	4	5	8	1
2	4	6	3	8	9	1	7	5
3	1	9	2	5	7	8	4	6
5	8	7	6	4	1	9	2	3
1	7	8	4	9	6	3	5	2
4	3	5	8	1	2	6	9	7
6	9	2	7	3	5	4	1	8

Page 24 — 21. LITTLE KILLER

2	8	6	5	1	3	4	9	7
7	9	5	4	2	8	3	1	6
1	4	3	9	7	6	8	5	2
9	2	8	3	6	4	1	7	5
3	6	1	7	5	2	9	8	4
5	7	4	1	8	9	2	6	3
4	5	7	8	3	1	6	2	9
8	3	2	6	9	5	7	4	1
6	1	9	2	4	7	5	3	8

Page 25 — 22. TOUCHY

6	1	7	4	9	5	3	2	8
2	3	8	1	7	6	4	9	5
4	9	5	3	2	8	7	6	1
5	6	2	9	4	3	1	8	7
9	4	1	8	6	7	5	3	2
7	8	3	5	1	2	9	4	6
1	2	6	7	3	4	8	5	9
3	5	9	2	8	1	6	7	4
8	7	4	6	5	9	2	1	3

Page 26 — 23. ODD-EVEN

3	7	4	6	9	8	5	1	2
5	1	8	3	2	7	4	9	6
9	2	6	4	1	5	8	3	7
8	3	5	1	7	4	2	6	9
6	9	2	8	5	3	7	4	1
1	4	7	2	6	9	3	5	8
2	5	9	7	3	6	1	8	4
7	8	3	9	4	1	6	2	5
4	6	1	5	8	2	9	7	3

Page 27 — 24. KROPKI

1	4	7	3	8	9	5	6	2
6	9	5	2	1	7	8	3	4
3	2	8	4	6	5	1	9	7
2	8	9	7	3	6	4	5	1
5	1	3	9	4	2	6	7	8
4	7	6	8	5	1	3	2	9
7	6	1	5	9	8	2	4	3
8	3	2	6	7	4	9	1	5
9	5	4	1	2	3	7	8	6

4	9	3	6	1	5	8	2	7
6	7	5	2	8	9	1	3	4
8	2	1	4	7	3	6	5	9
5	1	9	7	3	4	2	8	6
7	3	8	9	2	6	5	4	1
2	4	6	1	5	8	7	9	3
9	8	7	3	6	2	4	1	5
1	5	4	8	9	7	3	6	2
3	6	2	5	4	1	9	7	8

4	6	3	7	5	9	2	8	1
9	7	1	2	3	8	6	4	5
8	5	2	6	1	4	3	7	9
3	9	7	1	4	6	8	5	2
2	4	5	8	9	3	7	1	6
6	1	8	5	7	2	4	9	3
1	2	6	9	8	7	5	3	4
5	8	4	3	6	1	9	2	7
7	3	9	4	2	5	1	6	8

1	9	6	2	3	8	7	5	4
7	5	8	9	1	4	6	3	2
2	4	3	5	7	6	9	1	8
5	1	9	6	4	3	8	2	7
8	3	4	7	9	2	5	6	1
6	2	7	1	8	5	4	9	3
9	8	2	4	6	1	3	7	5
3	7	5	8	2	9	1	4	6
4	6	1	3	5	7	2	8	9

8	9	3	2	6	7	4	5	1
4	1	5	3	9	8	7	6	2
6	7	2	1	5	4	9	3	8
9	3	7	5	8	6	2	1	4
5	8	4	7	2	1	6	9	3
1	2	6	9	4	3	5	8	7
2	4	9	8	3	5	1	7	6
3	5	1	6	7	2	8	4	9
7	6	8	4	1	9	3	2	5

9	2	7	1	6	3	5	4	8
4	3	8	7	9	5	6	1	2
6	5	1	2	4	8	9	7	3
3	8	5	4	2	9	7	6	1
7	1	9	5	3	6	2	8	4
2	6	4	8	1	7	3	9	5
8	9	6	3	5	4	1	2	7
5	4	2	6	7	1	8	3	9
1	7	3	9	8	2	4	5	6

6	4	2	9	1	5	3	7	8
7	9	1	4	8	3	6	5	2
8	3	5	2	7	6	4	1	9
1	5	6	3	9	8	7	2	4
4	8	9	1	2	7	5	3	6
3	2	7	6	5	4	8	9	1
9	7	8	5	4	2	1	6	3
2	6	4	7	3	1	9	8	5
5	1	3	8	6	9	2	4	7

3	4	9	8	2	5	6	7	1
2	7	6	1	9	4	8	5	3
5	1	8	3	6	7	9	2	4
9	6	2	5	4	1	3	8	7
1	8	7	9	3	2	5	4	6
4	3	5	6	7	8	1	9	2
6	2	1	4	5	9	7	3	8
7	5	3	2	8	6	4	1	9
8	9	4	7	1	3	2	6	5

5	1	6	4	8	2	3	7	9
7	4	3	9	1	5	2	8	6
8	9	2	3	6	7	4	1	5
2	3	1	8	5	4	9	6	7
6	7	9	2	3	1	8	5	4
4	5	8	7	9	6	1	2	3
3	8	7	5	2	9	6	4	1
9	6	4	1	7	8	5	3	2
1	2	5	6	4	3	7	9	8

SOLUTIONS

Page 36 — 33. JIGSAW

2	1	8	4	3	9	7	6	5
5	7	1	2	4	8	9	3	6
9	3	6	5	7	4	8	1	2
6	5	3	7	8	2	1	4	9
7	6	4	1	9	5	2	8	3
4	9	2	3	1	6	5	7	8
3	8	9	6	5	7	4	2	1
8	2	7	9	6	1	3	5	4
1	4	5	8	2	3	6	9	7

Page 37 — 34. XV

9	5	7	1	4	6	2	3	8
2	8	6	5	7	3	4	9	1
3	1	4	8	9	2	7	5	6
5	7	2	6	3	4	1	8	9
4	9	3	7	8	1	5	6	2
1	6	8	9	2	5	3	4	7
6	2	9	4	5	7	8	1	3
7	4	1	3	6	8	9	2	5
8	3	5	2	1	9	6	7	4

Page 38 — 35. ARROWS

2	3	5	8	6	7	9	1	4
4	1	6	5	3	9	7	2	8
7	9	8	1	2	4	3	6	5
8	5	4	3	9	2	6	7	1
3	2	7	4	1	6	5	8	9
1	6	9	7	5	8	2	4	3
5	8	2	6	4	3	1	9	7
9	4	1	2	7	5	8	3	6
6	7	3	9	8	1	4	5	2

Page 39 — 36. BLACKOUT

9	5	8	3	■	6	2	1	7
■	1	4	5	2	8	9	6	3
7	3	2	9	1	4	■	5	8
5	4	■	2	7	1	8	3	9
8	2	6	4	3	5	7	■	1
3	9	1	8	6	■	5	2	4
6	7	5	1	8	2	3	9	■
2	8	3	■	9	7	6	4	5
4	■	9	6	5	3	1	8	2

Page 40 — 37. ODD-EVEN

7	4	8	9	3	2	5	1	6
3	6	1	7	5	8	2	9	4
2	9	5	6	4	1	8	3	7
5	8	4	3	1	6	9	7	2
9	7	3	8	2	4	1	6	5
6	1	2	5	7	9	4	8	3
4	2	7	1	8	3	6	5	9
1	3	9	4	6	5	7	2	8
8	5	6	2	9	7	3	4	1

Page 41 — 38. WRAPAROUND

1	4	2	6	8	5	9	7	3
5	8	7	2	6	4	1	3	9
4	5	1	9	3	7	6	2	8
7	6	9	1	5	3	4	8	2
6	2	3	7	4	9	8	1	5
2	9	4	3	7	8	5	6	1
9	1	8	5	2	6	3	4	7
8	3	5	4	1	2	7	9	6
3	7	6	8	9	1	2	5	4

Page 42 — 39. OUTSIDER

5	2	7	1	6	4	9	3	8
3	8	9	5	7	2	4	6	1
4	6	1	3	8	9	2	5	7
8	5	3	6	4	7	1	9	2
1	9	4	2	3	5	8	7	6
6	7	2	8	9	1	5	4	3
9	4	8	7	1	3	6	2	5
7	1	5	4	2	6	3	8	9
2	3	6	9	5	8	7	1	4

Page 43 — 40. CORNERED

1	7	3	9	5	8	4	2	6
4	2	9	6	7	1	3	5	8
6	5	8	3	4	2	1	7	9
8	6	4	1	3	5	2	9	7
7	9	5	8	2	4	6	3	1
2	3	1	7	9	6	5	8	4
3	4	6	5	8	7	9	1	2
5	1	7	2	6	9	8	4	3
9	8	2	4	1	3	7	6	5

41. FRAME

7	6	9	3	8	5	4	1	2
1	2	8	4	9	7	6	3	5
3	5	4	6	2	1	7	9	8
4	1	2	8	6	9	3	5	7
8	3	7	1	5	4	9	2	6
6	9	5	2	7	3	8	4	1
9	8	6	5	4	2	1	7	3
5	7	1	9	3	8	2	6	4
2	4	3	7	1	6	5	8	9

42. INEQUALITY

9	3	1	4	7	2	6	5	8
6	2	8	9	3	5	4	1	7
5	4	7	8	6	1	2	3	9
4	7	2	3	9	6	5	8	1
8	9	5	2	1	7	3	6	4
3	1	6	5	4	8	9	7	2
1	8	9	6	2	3	7	4	5
2	5	3	7	8	4	1	9	6
7	6	4	1	5	9	8	2	3

43. CONSECUTIVE

8	7	2	4	1	5	3	6	9
3	1	9	7	2	6	5	4	8
4	5	6	9	3	8	7	1	2
1	9	4	5	6	7	2	8	3
7	8	3	1	9	2	6	5	4
2	6	5	3	8	4	9	7	1
5	3	7	2	4	1	8	9	6
6	2	1	8	7	9	4	3	5
9	4	8	6	5	3	1	2	7

44. JIGSAW

1	8	9	5	2	6	4	7	3
7	2	6	9	3	8	5	4	1
5	4	3	1	7	2	6	9	8
2	5	7	4	8	9	3	1	6
3	1	8	6	5	7	9	2	4
6	9	4	2	1	3	8	5	7
9	3	5	8	4	1	7	6	2
8	6	2	7	9	4	1	3	5
4	7	1	3	6	5	2	8	9

45. XV

5	8	6	7	4	1	2	9	3
2	3	7	5	9	8	6	4	1
9	1	4	3	2	6	5	7	8
4	5	9	1	7	2	8	3	6
1	7	8	6	3	4	9	2	5
3	6	2	8	5	9	4	1	7
6	9	5	2	1	3	7	8	4
8	4	1	9	6	7	3	5	2
7	2	3	4	8	5	1	6	9

46. SLASHED

2	4	3	5	7	6	8	9	1
9	6	1	4	8	2	7	3	5
8	5	7	3	1	9	4	2	6
4	2	8	9	6	7	1	5	3
1	7	6	2	3	5	9	4	8
5	3	9	1	4	8	2	6	7
7	1	4	6	9	3	5	8	2
3	8	2	7	5	4	6	1	9
6	9	5	8	2	1	3	7	4

47. THERMOMETER

5	2	7	3	1	6	8	9	4
6	4	8	9	2	5	1	3	7
1	9	3	7	8	4	2	6	5
3	7	9	2	5	1	6	4	8
4	5	6	8	9	7	3	2	1
2	8	1	4	6	3	5	7	9
9	3	5	6	7	8	4	1	2
8	6	2	1	4	9	7	5	3
7	1	4	5	3	2	9	8	6

48. TRIO

2	6	4	8	9	7	1	5	3
5	9	1	2	3	6	7	4	8
3	7	8	1	5	4	2	9	6
9	2	3	5	7	8	6	1	4
6	1	7	4	2	3	9	8	5
8	4	5	9	6	1	3	7	2
7	8	6	3	1	5	4	2	9
4	3	2	7	8	9	5	6	1
1	5	9	6	4	2	8	3	7

SOLUTIONS

Page 52 — 49. TOUCHY

1	3	8	9	5	6	2	4	7
6	9	4	2	7	8	5	1	3
7	2	5	3	1	4	6	8	9
3	4	6	8	2	9	7	5	1
5	8	9	7	6	1	4	3	2
2	7	1	5	4	3	8	9	6
8	5	3	6	9	2	1	7	4
4	6	7	1	3	5	9	2	8
9	1	2	4	8	7	3	6	5

Page 53 — 50. ARROWS

7	1	6	8	3	2	5	4	9
8	5	9	1	4	7	3	2	6
4	3	2	9	6	5	7	1	8
6	8	7	3	1	4	2	9	5
2	4	3	5	7	9	8	6	1
1	9	5	2	8	6	4	3	7
3	6	4	7	5	1	9	8	2
9	7	1	4	2	8	6	5	3
5	2	8	6	9	3	1	7	4

Page 54 — 51. THERMOMETER

3	4	8	5	2	9	6	7	1
9	6	5	4	7	1	8	2	3
7	2	1	6	8	3	5	4	9
8	1	2	3	6	4	7	9	5
5	7	3	9	1	8	2	6	4
6	9	4	7	5	2	3	1	8
4	3	6	2	9	5	1	8	7
2	8	9	1	3	7	4	5	6
1	5	7	8	4	6	9	3	2

Page 55 — 52. KROPKI

6	9	8	3	5	2	4	7	1
4	3	5	9	1	7	8	6	2
7	2	1	6	8	4	3	5	9
3	4	2	1	7	5	6	9	8
9	1	7	8	3	6	5	2	4
5	8	6	4	2	9	7	1	3
1	6	3	7	9	8	2	4	5
8	5	4	2	6	1	9	3	7
2	7	9	5	4	3	1	8	6

Page 56 — 53. QUAD MARKS

7	2	8	9	4	3	5	1	6
4	1	9	5	6	2	8	3	7
3	5	6	1	8	7	4	2	9
5	3	2	4	9	6	7	8	1
8	6	7	3	2	1	9	5	4
1	9	4	7	5	8	3	6	2
9	8	1	6	7	5	2	4	3
6	7	5	2	3	4	1	9	8
2	4	3	8	1	9	6	7	5

Page 57 — 54. LITTLE KILLER

1	7	6	8	2	5	3	9	4
5	9	2	4	6	3	8	7	1
3	8	4	1	9	7	2	5	6
7	1	9	3	4	8	6	2	5
6	4	3	2	5	1	9	8	7
8	2	5	9	7	6	4	1	3
4	5	1	6	8	9	7	3	2
2	3	8	7	1	4	5	6	9
9	6	7	5	3	2	1	4	8

Page 58 — 55. SLASHED

1	2	7	3	8	6	4	9	5
4	8	5	9	7	1	2	6	3
9	6	3	4	2	5	7	1	8
2	1	9	6	3	4	8	5	7
3	7	6	8	5	9	1	4	2
5	4	8	2	1	7	6	3	9
7	3	1	5	4	2	9	8	6
6	5	4	7	9	8	3	2	1
8	9	2	1	6	3	5	7	4

Page 59 — 56. BLACKOUT

6	5	2	1	7	4	3	8	▓
8	7	1	2	9	▓	4	5	6
9	▓	4	5	6	3	2	7	1
▓	9	3	4	8	7	1	6	2
1	4	5	6	▓	2	8	3	9
2	6	8	9	3	1	▓	4	5
4	2	6	3	1	9	5	▓	7
7	3	9	▓	4	5	6	2	8
5	8	▓	7	2	6	9	1	4

Page 60 — 57. WRAPAROUND

1	5	9	3	7	6	2	8	4
9	3	1	7	8	4	6	2	5
2	6	4	1	9	5	7	3	8
7	8	5	9	2	3	4	1	6
4	1	8	5	6	9	3	7	2
5	2	7	4	1	8	9	6	3
3	7	2	6	5	1	8	4	9
6	9	3	8	4	2	1	5	7
8	4	6	2	3	7	5	9	1

Page 61 — 58. CONSECUTIVE

6	2	7	9	3	5	8	4	1
3	5	8	7	4	1	9	2	6
9	1	4	2	6	8	3	7	5
5	7	1	8	2	4	6	3	9
4	3	9	1	7	6	5	8	2
2	8	6	5	9	3	7	1	4
1	4	3	6	5	7	2	9	8
8	6	2	3	1	9	4	5	7
7	9	5	4	8	2	1	6	3

Page 62 — 59. CORNERED

5	7	9	1	8	3	4	6	2
2	3	6	4	5	9	7	1	8
1	8	4	6	2	7	3	5	9
7	6	1	2	3	4	9	8	5
4	9	2	8	6	5	1	3	7
3	5	8	9	7	1	6	2	4
6	4	5	3	9	2	8	7	1
9	2	3	7	1	8	5	4	6
8	1	7	5	4	6	2	9	3

Page 63 — 60. OUTSIDER

4	7	1	8	3	9	6	2	5
2	8	3	7	6	5	4	9	1
9	5	6	4	2	1	3	8	7
1	6	7	2	8	4	9	5	3
3	2	4	9	5	6	7	1	8
5	9	8	1	7	3	2	6	4
8	4	5	3	9	2	1	7	6
6	3	2	5	1	7	8	4	9
7	1	9	6	4	8	5	3	2

Page 64 — 61. JIGSAW

8	2	1	9	5	7	6	4	3
4	3	5	7	6	9	2	1	8
7	6	3	2	4	5	9	8	1
1	8	9	4	3	2	7	6	5
6	1	2	8	9	3	4	5	7
5	7	4	3	1	6	8	2	9
9	5	6	1	8	4	3	7	2
2	9	8	6	7	1	5	3	4
3	4	7	5	2	8	1	9	6

Page 65 — 62. TOUCHY

4	7	2	6	8	3	9	5	1
1	6	3	9	2	5	8	4	7
5	9	8	1	4	7	2	6	3
6	3	5	7	9	8	4	1	2
9	2	4	3	6	1	7	8	5
8	1	7	2	5	4	6	3	9
3	5	6	8	7	9	1	2	4
7	8	1	4	3	2	5	9	6
2	4	9	5	1	6	3	7	8

Page 66 — 63. ARROWS

7	2	5	4	8	1	3	6	9
8	4	6	9	2	3	7	1	5
3	9	1	5	7	6	4	8	2
2	7	4	6	1	9	8	5	3
9	1	3	8	5	4	6	2	7
5	6	8	2	3	7	9	4	1
6	3	2	1	9	8	5	7	4
4	5	7	3	6	2	1	9	8
1	8	9	7	4	5	2	3	6

Page 67 — 64. FRAME

7	4	5	8	9	3	6	2	1
8	2	1	7	6	4	9	5	3
3	6	9	2	5	1	8	7	4
4	8	7	1	2	6	5	3	9
2	1	6	9	3	5	7	4	8
5	9	3	4	7	8	1	6	2
6	5	4	3	8	9	2	1	7
1	7	8	5	4	2	3	9	6
9	3	2	6	1	7	4	8	5

SOLUTIONS

Page 68 — 65. INEQUALITY

1	4	9	3	6	8	7	5	2
5	8	2	4	1	7	6	3	9
6	7	3	5	2	9	4	8	1
4	9	1	8	3	5	2	6	7
2	3	6	7	4	1	8	9	5
7	5	8	2	9	6	3	1	4
3	1	5	6	7	4	9	2	8
8	6	4	9	5	2	1	7	3
9	2	7	1	8	3	5	4	6

Page 69 — 66. XV

7	3	2	8	5	9	4	6	1
4	6	9	2	3	1	8	5	7
8	1	5	6	7	4	2	3	9
3	9	4	1	2	8	5	7	6
5	2	8	7	6	3	9	1	4
1	7	6	4	9	5	3	8	2
6	4	3	5	1	2	7	9	8
9	8	7	3	4	6	1	2	5
2	5	1	9	8	7	6	4	3

Page 70 — 67. TRIO

2	4	8	6	5	1	3	7	9
9	3	6	8	7	2	4	1	5
7	5	1	4	3	9	8	2	6
3	6	9	1	2	4	5	8	7
5	2	4	7	9	8	1	6	3
1	8	7	5	6	3	2	9	4
4	7	2	3	1	6	9	5	8
8	9	5	2	4	7	6	3	1
6	1	3	9	8	5	7	4	2

Page 71 — 68. ODD-EVEN

8	3	6	2	9	4	5	1	7
9	4	1	8	5	7	2	3	6
5	2	7	3	6	1	9	4	8
2	6	8	9	1	5	3	7	4
7	9	3	6	4	2	1	8	5
4	1	5	7	3	8	6	9	2
1	8	4	5	2	3	7	6	9
6	7	2	1	8	9	4	5	3
3	5	9	4	7	6	8	2	1

Page 72 — 69. TOUCHY

8	2	9	1	5	3	6	7	4
3	6	5	2	7	4	1	8	9
7	1	4	6	9	8	5	2	3
6	5	8	7	4	2	3	9	1
9	7	2	3	6	1	4	5	8
4	3	1	9	8	5	7	6	2
5	8	6	4	3	9	2	1	7
2	9	3	5	1	7	8	4	6
1	4	7	8	2	6	9	3	5

Page 73 — 70. XV

7	9	3	1	8	4	5	6	2
2	1	4	6	5	3	7	8	9
8	5	6	9	2	7	4	3	1
9	8	5	3	7	1	2	4	6
6	7	1	2	4	5	3	9	8
4	3	2	8	6	9	1	7	5
5	6	7	4	9	2	8	1	3
1	4	9	5	3	8	6	2	7
3	2	8	7	1	6	9	5	4

Page 74 — 71. CONSECUTIVE

2	9	3	7	1	6	5	8	4
6	5	1	8	3	4	2	9	7
8	4	7	9	5	2	1	6	3
4	2	6	5	9	1	7	3	8
3	7	5	6	4	8	9	2	1
9	1	8	3	2	7	6	4	5
1	6	2	4	8	5	3	7	9
7	3	4	1	6	9	8	5	2
5	8	9	2	7	3	4	1	6

Page 75 — 72. CORNERED

2	6	1	5	8	3	9	4	7
9	8	3	4	7	1	6	2	5
7	5	4	9	2	6	1	8	3
1	2	6	3	9	8	7	5	4
3	4	8	6	5	7	2	9	1
5	7	9	1	4	2	3	6	8
6	9	7	8	3	4	5	1	2
4	1	2	7	6	5	8	3	9
8	3	5	2	1	9	4	7	6

73. BLACKOUT

6	2	9	4		5	3	1	7
3	1	4	7	9	6	2	8	
7		8	2	3	1	5	9	4
2	6	1	8	4	7	9		3
5	8	7	3	6		1	4	2
	4	3	1	5	9	7	6	8
9	5		6	7	3	4	2	1
4	7	2	9	1	8		3	6
1	3	6		2	4	8	7	5

74. OUTSIDER

8	5	3	1	7	6	9	2	4
4	7	2	5	9	3	8	1	6
9	1	6	8	4	2	5	7	3
6	9	5	4	2	7	1	3	8
2	3	1	6	8	5	4	9	7
7	4	8	9	3	1	2	6	5
1	8	7	3	5	9	6	4	2
5	2	9	7	6	4	3	8	1
3	6	4	2	1	8	7	5	9

75. QUAD MARKS

4	3	7	9	6	5	2	1	8
2	9	8	1	3	4	5	7	6
6	1	5	2	7	8	3	4	9
8	4	3	6	2	1	7	9	5
1	7	6	5	9	3	4	8	2
5	2	9	8	4	7	1	6	3
9	6	1	7	5	2	8	3	4
3	8	2	4	1	9	6	5	7
7	5	4	3	8	6	9	2	1

76. JIGSAW

3	9	7	8	2	6	4	1	5
5	8	4	6	1	7	2	9	3
1	6	3	9	5	2	8	7	4
8	4	5	2	3	9	7	6	1
9	1	6	4	7	8	5	3	2
7	3	2	1	8	4	6	5	9
2	5	9	7	6	1	3	4	8
6	2	1	3	4	5	9	8	7
4	7	8	5	9	3	1	2	6

77. FRAME

9	3	5	4	8	7	1	2	6
8	4	6	3	2	1	5	7	9
7	2	1	5	6	9	8	3	4
3	6	8	2	7	5	4	9	1
4	7	2	9	1	8	3	6	5
5	1	9	6	3	4	7	8	2
1	5	3	7	9	6	2	4	8
2	9	4	8	5	3	6	1	7
6	8	7	1	4	2	9	5	3

78. ARROWS

6	4	8	3	2	9	1	7	5
2	5	7	1	8	6	4	9	3
9	1	3	4	7	5	6	8	2
1	9	4	8	6	3	2	5	7
3	7	5	9	1	2	8	4	6
8	2	6	7	5	4	9	3	1
7	6	9	5	4	1	3	2	8
5	3	1	2	9	8	7	6	4
4	8	2	6	3	7	5	1	9

79. ODD-EVEN

8	1	5	6	7	9	2	3	4
2	7	6	8	4	3	9	5	1
9	4	3	2	1	5	8	6	7
1	6	4	7	9	8	5	2	3
5	3	8	4	6	2	7	1	9
7	9	2	5	3	1	4	8	6
3	2	1	9	8	4	6	7	5
4	8	7	1	5	6	3	9	2
6	5	9	3	2	7	1	4	8

80. CONSECUTIVE

1	2	7	8	4	3	5	9	6
3	9	8	6	1	5	4	7	2
6	5	4	7	2	9	8	1	3
2	4	1	5	6	8	9	3	7
7	8	5	3	9	2	1	6	4
9	6	3	4	7	1	2	5	8
4	1	9	2	3	7	6	8	5
5	3	6	1	8	4	7	2	9
8	7	2	9	5	6	3	4	1

SOLUTIONS

Page 84 — 81. QUAD MARKS

2	4	8	9	1	6	3	5	7
5	1	3	4	2	7	6	8	9
6	9	7	3	8	5	1	4	2
8	5	2	6	3	1	9	7	4
1	7	6	5	4	9	8	2	3
9	3	4	2	7	8	5	6	1
3	6	9	7	5	4	2	1	8
7	2	1	8	6	3	4	9	5
4	8	5	1	9	2	7	3	6

Page 85 — 82. LITTLE KILLER

8	5	6	2	4	1	9	3	7
2	7	1	9	6	3	4	5	8
9	4	3	8	7	5	2	6	1
4	1	9	6	8	7	5	2	3
5	8	7	3	2	4	1	9	6
3	6	2	1	5	9	7	8	4
7	9	4	5	3	8	6	1	2
1	2	8	7	9	6	3	4	5
6	3	5	4	1	2	8	7	9

Page 86 — 83. WRAPAROUND

9	1	6	4	3	5	7	2	8
1	5	4	8	7	2	6	3	9
6	3	7	9	1	8	2	5	4
3	7	8	2	9	1	5	4	6
5	9	2	1	4	6	8	7	3
2	4	3	6	8	7	1	9	5
4	6	1	7	5	9	3	8	2
7	8	5	3	2	4	9	6	1
8	2	9	5	6	3	4	1	7

Page 87 — 84. FRAME

3	6	5	4	7	9	1	2	8
9	4	7	2	8	1	6	3	5
1	2	8	5	3	6	7	9	4
7	8	6	9	2	4	3	5	1
4	1	2	3	5	8	9	7	6
5	9	3	1	6	7	4	8	2
8	3	9	6	4	5	2	1	7
2	5	4	7	1	3	8	6	9
6	7	1	8	9	2	5	4	3

Page 88 — 85. ARROWS

3	6	8	5	7	2	9	1	4
9	2	7	4	3	1	8	6	5
1	5	4	9	6	8	7	3	2
8	7	9	6	2	4	3	5	1
4	1	6	3	9	5	2	7	8
2	3	5	8	1	7	6	4	9
6	8	3	1	4	9	5	2	7
7	9	1	2	5	3	4	8	6
5	4	2	7	8	6	1	9	3

Page 89 — 86. TOUCHY

6	2	4	9	8	7	1	5	3
3	5	8	1	2	6	4	9	7
1	9	7	5	4	3	8	6	2
8	6	3	2	1	9	5	7	4
2	1	5	6	7	4	3	8	9
4	7	9	3	5	8	2	1	6
9	8	2	4	6	1	7	3	5
7	4	6	8	3	5	9	2	1
5	3	1	7	9	2	6	4	8

Page 90 — 87. JIGSAW

7	3	1	9	5	6	4	2	8
5	2	8	1	6	4	7	9	3
2	5	7	3	4	8	9	6	1
3	8	4	7	9	5	6	1	2
1	9	6	4	2	7	3	8	5
4	6	9	8	1	3	2	5	7
9	1	3	6	8	2	5	7	4
6	7	2	5	3	1	8	4	9
8	4	5	2	7	9	1	3	6

Page 91 — 88. SLASHED

3	5	4	9	6	7	1	8	2
9	1	6	2	8	4	3	5	7
8	2	7	3	5	1	9	6	4
4	9	8	6	7	3	2	1	5
5	6	1	4	2	9	8	7	3
2	7	3	5	1	8	4	9	6
7	4	9	8	3	6	5	2	1
6	3	5	1	9	2	7	4	8
1	8	2	7	4	5	6	3	9

Page 92 — 89. INEQUALITY

7	5	2	6	8	3	4	9	1
4	9	1	7	2	5	6	8	3
3	8	6	9	1	4	5	7	2
2	3	9	1	6	8	7	4	5
1	6	8	4	5	7	3	2	9
5	4	7	2	3	9	1	6	8
9	7	5	8	4	1	2	3	6
6	1	4	3	9	2	8	5	7
8	2	3	5	7	6	9	1	4

Page 93 — 90. BLACKOUT

2	3	1		7	4	6	9	5
7	4	6	8	9	5	1		3
9		8	6	3	1	7	2	4
3	5	9	2	8	6		1	7
6	1	7	4		9	3	8	2
8	2		3	1	7	5	4	9
1	7	5	9	4	8	2	3	
	8	2	7	6	3	4	5	1
4	6	3	1	5		9	7	8

Page 94 — 91. XV

2	4	9	5	1	7	8	3	6
5	8	7	6	9	3	1	4	2
3	6	1	4	2	8	5	9	7
8	3	6	1	4	9	2	7	5
1	2	4	3	7	5	6	8	9
9	7	5	2	8	6	4	1	3
6	1	2	9	3	4	7	5	8
4	9	8	7	5	2	3	6	1
7	5	3	8	6	1	9	2	4

Page 95 — 92. CORNERED

6	3	1	4	9	2	5	7	8
8	2	9	7	5	1	4	3	6
4	5	7	3	6	8	2	9	1
2	6	5	1	3	9	7	8	4
9	1	8	5	7	4	3	6	2
7	4	3	8	2	6	1	5	9
1	7	6	2	8	5	9	4	3
3	8	2	9	4	7	6	1	5
5	9	4	6	1	3	8	2	7

Page 96 — 93. OUTSIDER

3	7	5	1	4	6	9	2	8
2	8	1	3	7	9	5	6	4
4	9	6	5	8	2	7	1	3
1	6	9	4	2	7	8	3	5
8	3	7	6	9	5	2	4	1
5	2	4	8	1	3	6	7	9
9	1	3	2	6	8	4	5	7
6	5	8	7	3	4	1	9	2
7	4	2	9	5	1	3	8	6

Page 97 — 94. FRAME

9	4	7	5	1	6	8	3	2
1	6	2	3	7	8	5	4	9
5	8	3	2	4	9	7	1	6
6	2	4	8	5	7	3	9	1
8	3	9	6	2	1	4	7	5
7	5	1	9	3	4	6	2	8
4	7	8	1	9	5	2	6	3
2	9	5	7	6	3	1	8	4
3	1	6	4	8	2	9	5	7

Page 98 — 95. CONSECUTIVE

9	3	6	5	1	7	4	2	8
7	8	2	4	3	6	1	9	5
5	4	1	9	8	2	3	7	6
6	9	8	1	7	4	2	5	3
4	7	5	3	2	9	8	6	1
2	1	3	8	6	5	9	4	7
1	5	9	7	4	3	6	8	2
8	6	4	2	5	1	7	3	9
3	2	7	6	9	8	5	1	4

Page 99 — 96. WRAPAROUND

5	8	4	1	6	9	3	2	7
9	4	1	3	8	5	7	6	2
1	6	9	7	3	2	8	4	5
3	9	7	2	4	6	1	5	8
4	2	8	6	5	7	9	1	3
6	5	3	9	1	8	2	7	4
7	1	5	4	2	3	6	8	9
2	7	6	8	9	4	5	3	1
8	3	2	5	7	1	4	9	6

SOLUTIONS

Page 100 — 97. THERMOMETER

1	2	7	4	9	5	3	6	8
4	8	9	7	3	6	5	1	2
6	3	5	2	8	1	4	9	7
5	9	1	3	7	4	2	8	6
8	4	6	5	1	2	7	3	9
3	7	2	9	6	8	1	5	4
7	6	8	1	4	3	9	2	5
2	1	4	8	5	9	6	7	3
9	5	3	6	2	7	8	4	1

Page 101 — 98. ARROWS

7	1	2	8	3	4	6	5	9
8	5	6	9	1	7	3	4	2
4	9	3	5	6	2	7	8	1
9	7	4	6	2	5	8	1	3
5	2	1	4	8	3	9	6	7
3	6	8	1	7	9	4	2	5
6	8	5	3	9	1	2	7	4
2	4	9	7	5	8	1	3	6
1	3	7	2	4	6	5	9	8

Page 102 — 99. KROPKI

8	6	2	1	5	9	3	7	4
7	3	4	6	2	8	9	5	1
5	9	1	7	4	3	6	8	2
2	1	8	9	7	4	5	6	3
9	7	3	5	6	2	4	1	8
4	5	6	8	3	1	2	9	7
3	8	9	4	1	6	7	2	5
1	2	5	3	9	7	8	4	6
6	4	7	2	8	5	1	3	9

Page 103 — 100. XV

2	3	1	6	4	8	9	7	5
4	7	6	9	1	5	8	3	2
5	8	9	3	2	7	1	6	4
6	4	8	1	5	3	7	2	9
1	5	2	4	7	9	3	8	6
3	9	7	8	6	2	4	5	1
9	1	5	7	8	6	2	4	3
8	2	4	5	3	1	6	9	7
7	6	3	2	9	4	5	1	8

Page 104 — 101. TOUCHY

5	3	2	9	1	7	4	8	6
4	8	6	3	5	2	1	9	7
1	7	9	4	8	6	5	3	2
9	5	3	6	2	4	7	1	8
8	1	7	5	3	9	2	6	4
2	6	4	1	7	8	3	5	9
3	9	8	2	4	5	6	7	1
6	4	1	7	9	3	8	2	5
7	2	5	8	6	1	9	4	3

Page 105 — 102. SLASHED

9	5	7	6	3	4	8	1	2
8	4	1	5	2	9	6	3	7
6	2	3	7	8	1	5	9	4
7	1	9	8	6	2	3	4	5
2	6	8	4	5	3	9	7	1
4	3	5	9	1	7	2	6	8
5	9	4	2	7	6	1	8	3
3	8	6	1	4	5	7	2	9
1	7	2	3	9	8	4	5	6

Page 106 — 103. INEQUALITY

2	5	1	3	7	9	6	8	4
6	4	9	5	2	8	7	1	3
3	8	7	6	1	4	2	5	9
4	7	6	2	8	5	3	9	1
5	9	2	1	3	6	8	4	7
8	1	3	9	4	7	5	2	6
1	6	5	8	9	3	4	7	2
7	2	8	4	6	1	9	3	5
9	3	4	7	5	2	1	6	8

Page 107 — 104. CONSECUTIVE

8	6	1	4	3	5	9	7	2
4	3	9	7	6	2	5	1	8
7	5	2	8	1	9	4	3	6
5	1	8	3	7	6	2	4	9
6	2	4	1	9	8	3	5	7
3	9	7	2	5	4	8	6	1
1	7	5	9	2	3	6	8	4
9	4	6	5	8	1	7	2	3
2	8	3	6	4	7	1	9	5

105. QUAD MARKS

9	3	6	4	7	1	2	5	8
1	7	5	8	2	9	6	4	3
8	2	4	5	6	3	9	7	1
2	1	7	3	4	6	5	8	9
5	4	9	1	8	2	7	3	6
3	6	8	7	9	5	4	1	2
4	8	2	6	3	7	1	9	5
6	5	3	9	1	4	8	2	7
7	9	1	2	5	8	3	6	4

106. ODD-EVEN

1	6	8	2	4	3	7	9	5
4	3	2	9	7	5	1	8	6
7	9	5	1	6	8	4	2	3
2	8	4	5	3	7	9	6	1
9	5	3	6	2	1	8	4	7
6	7	1	8	9	4	5	3	2
5	4	6	3	1	9	2	7	8
3	1	7	4	8	2	6	5	9
8	2	9	7	5	6	3	1	4

107. JIGSAW

8	7	3	6	5	2	1	9	4
2	8	9	7	3	6	4	5	1
1	9	4	2	6	7	3	8	5
5	6	2	1	7	4	9	3	8
4	2	8	5	9	1	7	6	3
9	1	7	4	8	3	5	2	6
3	5	1	8	2	9	6	4	7
6	4	5	3	1	8	2	7	9
7	3	6	9	4	5	8	1	2

108. CORNERED

9	1	5	6	2	4	7	8	3
3	6	4	7	8	9	5	2	1
2	8	7	5	1	3	4	9	6
8	4	2	3	5	1	6	7	9
6	5	1	9	7	2	3	4	8
7	3	9	8	4	6	1	5	2
1	9	8	4	6	5	2	3	7
4	7	6	2	3	8	9	1	5
5	2	3	1	9	7	8	6	4

109. ARROWS

6	8	1	9	5	3	4	7	2
5	4	7	2	8	1	6	3	9
9	2	3	6	4	7	8	1	5
1	7	4	8	6	9	2	5	3
2	6	5	3	7	4	1	9	8
3	9	8	5	1	2	7	4	6
4	3	2	1	9	8	5	6	7
7	5	9	4	2	6	3	8	1
8	1	6	7	3	5	9	2	4

110. XV

7	2	1	8	4	5	9	3	6
9	8	3	6	2	7	5	4	1
6	4	5	9	1	3	2	7	8
1	3	4	7	5	2	6	8	9
5	9	7	4	6	8	3	1	2
8	6	2	1	3	9	4	5	7
3	7	9	2	8	4	1	6	5
4	1	8	5	9	6	7	2	3
2	5	6	3	7	1	8	9	4

SOLUTIONS

If you enjoyed **TWISTED SUDOKU** why not give **TWISTED WORD SEARCH** a whirl next?

TWISTED
SUDOKU